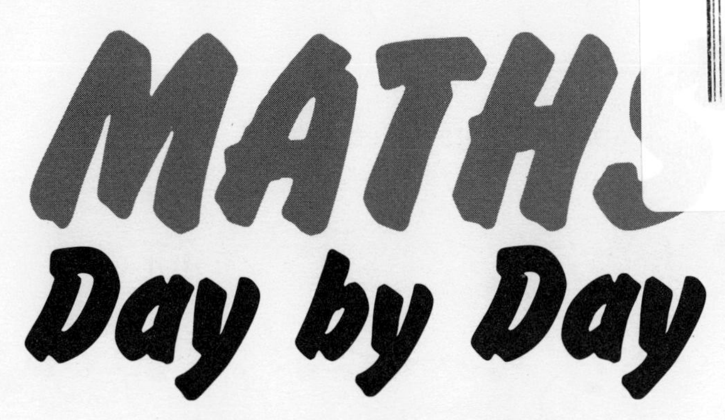

Dave Kirkby

Book One

This is what the symbols in this book mean.

 the skill you can learn from the activity

 what you need to do in this activity

 an example showing how to do the activity

Collins Educational
An imprint of HarperCollins*Publishers*

1 Counting

Counting up to 10.

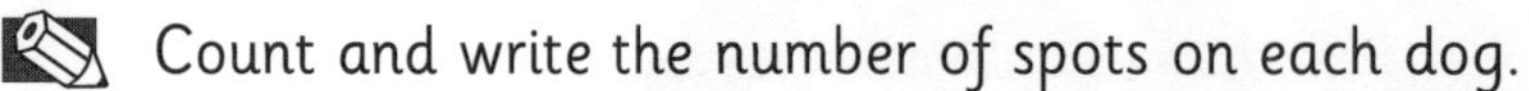

Count and write the number of spots on each dog.

Like this: *4*

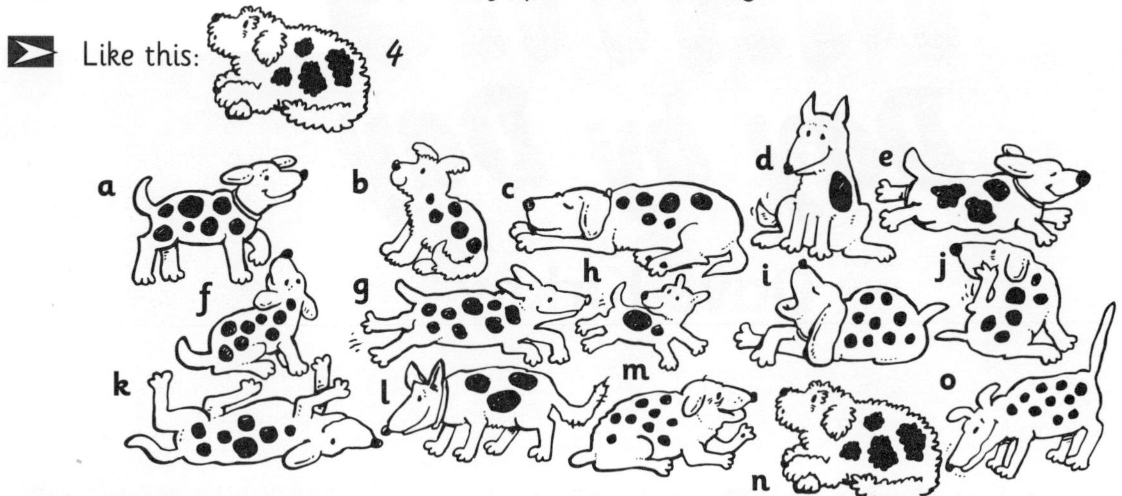

2 Writing numerals

Writing number names (up to 20) in numerals.

Write these number names in numerals.

Like this: thirteen *13*

a **five**	b eleven	c **two**	d *thirteen*
e *nine*	f **fifteen**	g three	h eighteen
i **ten**	j seven	k *twelve*	l *one*
m four	n *sixteen*	o **twenty**	p **fourteen**

3 Stamps

Adding two sums of money (totals up to 10p).

Here are 5 different stamps. 1p 2p 3p 4p 5p

Write the total cost of sending a letter with these pairs of stamps.

Like this: and *6p*

a and	b and	c and	d and
e and	f and	g and	h and
i and	j and	k and	l and

4 Put in order

Ordering numbers to 10.

Write the sets of numbers in order from **smallest** to **largest**.

Like this: 7 3 1 9 5 2 *1, 2, 3, 5, 7, 9*

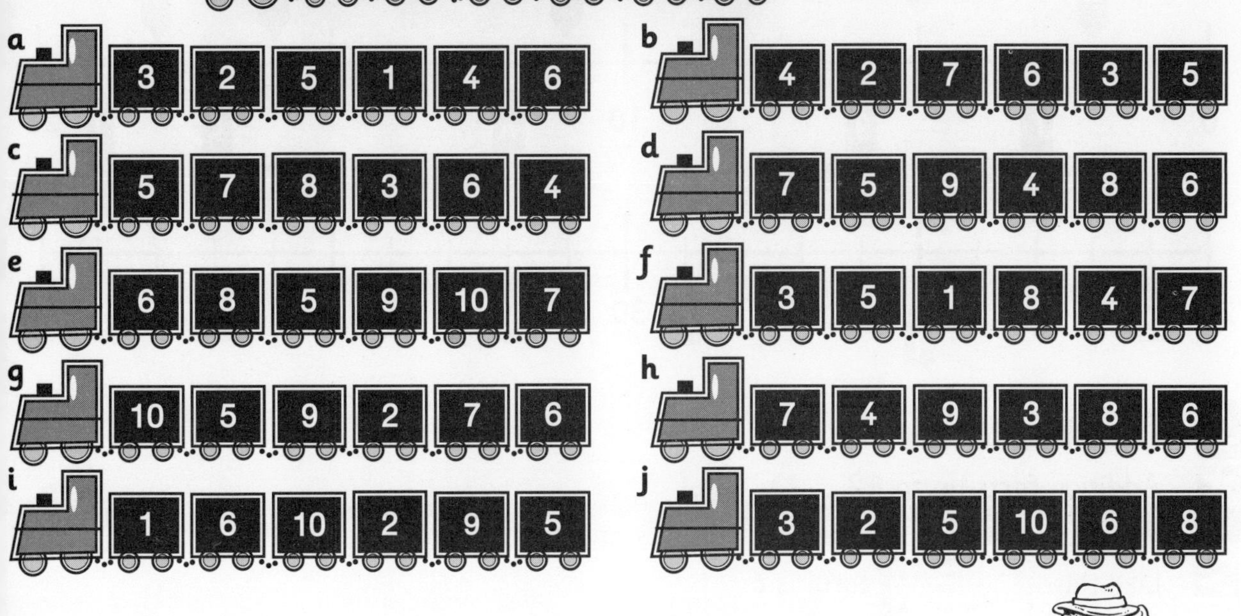

5 Dominoes

Recognising odd and even numbers.

Here is a set of dominoes without the blanks.

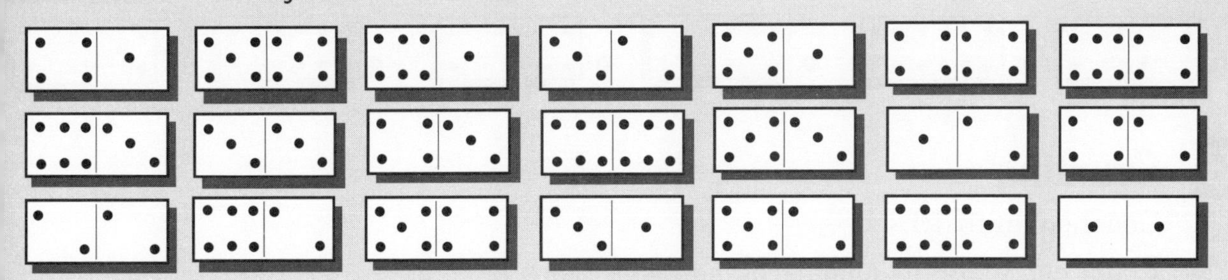

a Find dominoes which have an **odd** number of spots on **both** sides.

b Draw them. How many are there? Find and draw dominoes with an **even** number of spots on **both** sides.

c Find and draw dominoes with an **odd** number on one side, and an **even** number on the other side. How many are there?

1 Number lines

Finding points on a number line marked in ones.

Write the position of each letter on the lines.

Like this: **a** *2*

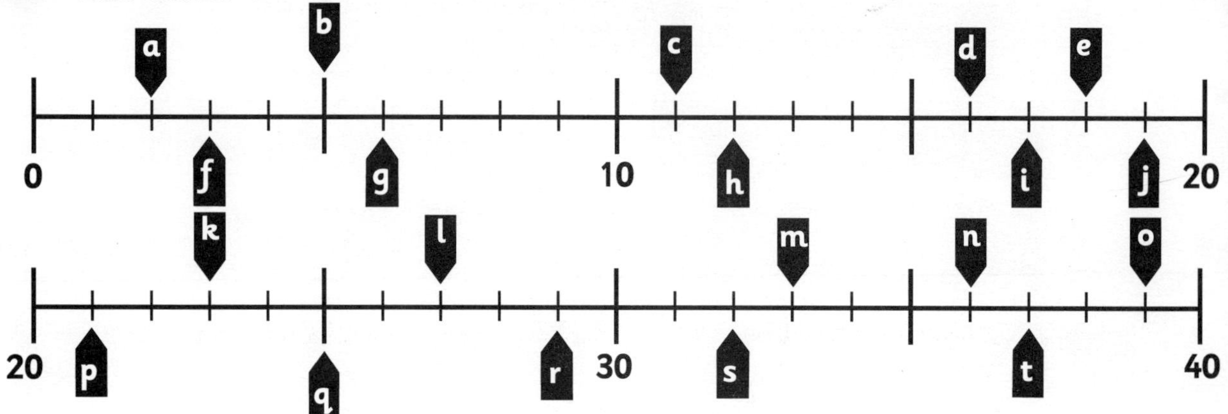

2 Domino totals

Addition facts up to 12.

Write the **total** of the number of spots on each domino.

Like this: [domino] total is *6*

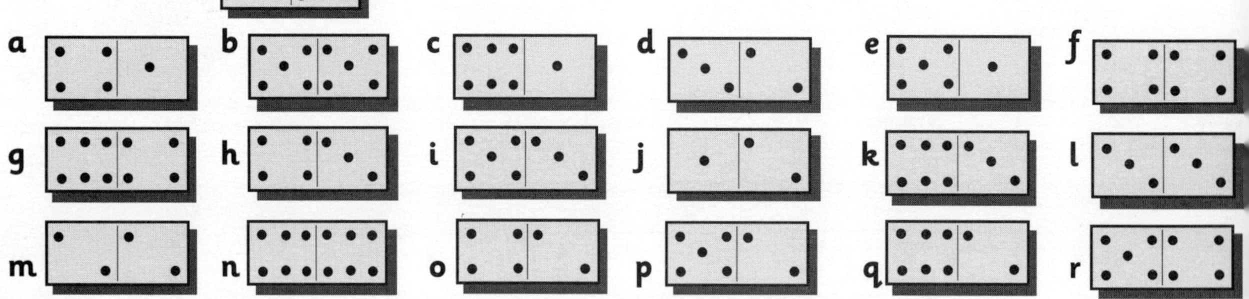

3 Counting

Counting up to 10.

Count and write the number of marbles in each picture.

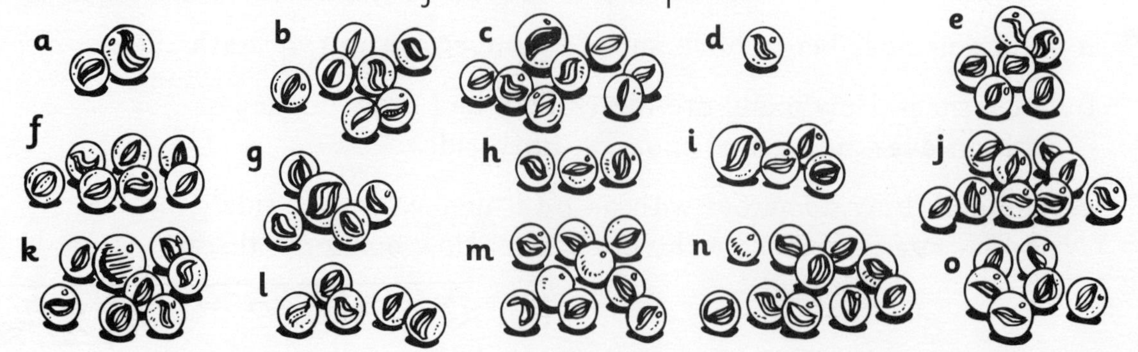

4 Sequences

Finding missing entries in a number sequence (steps of 1, 2).

Write the missing numbers in each sequence.

Like this: 56 57 w 59 60 x *w 58 x 61*

41	42	**a**	44	45	**b**
35	**c**	37	38	**d**	40
e	68	67	66	65	**f**
23	22	**g**	20	19	**h**
52	**i**	56	**j**	60	62
k	47	49	**l**	53	55
88	86	84	**m**	80	**n**
34	**o**	**p**	40	42	44
q	71	**r**	67	**s**	63
27	**t**	29	**u**	31	**v**

5 Stamps

3p 2p

Adding sums of money.

It will cost 9p to send your letter. You can use only **2p** and **3p** stamps.

Here are two ways of arranging the stamps.

a Find and show other ways.

b Now find and show ways of arranging the stamps on a letter which costs **7p**.

c Do the same for other letter costs.

1 Adding

Vertical addition (totals up to 10).

Copy and complete these additions.

Like this:

$$\begin{array}{r} 3 \\ +2 \\ \hline 5 \end{array}$$

a $\begin{array}{r} 8 \\ +1 \\ \hline \end{array}$ **b** $\begin{array}{r} 2 \\ +2 \\ \hline \end{array}$ **c** $\begin{array}{r} 2 \\ +7 \\ \hline \end{array}$ **d** $\begin{array}{r} 2 \\ +5 \\ \hline \end{array}$ **e** $\begin{array}{r} 4 \\ +3 \\ \hline \end{array}$ **f** $\begin{array}{r} 3 \\ +4 \\ \hline \end{array}$ **g** $\begin{array}{r} 3 \\ +6 \\ \hline \end{array}$ **h** $\begin{array}{r} 7 \\ +1 \\ \hline \end{array}$

i $\begin{array}{r} 1 \\ +8 \\ \hline \end{array}$ **j** $\begin{array}{r} 4 \\ +4 \\ \hline \end{array}$ **k** $\begin{array}{r} 2 \\ +3 \\ \hline \end{array}$ **l** $\begin{array}{r} 6 \\ +1 \\ \hline \end{array}$ **m** $\begin{array}{r} 6 \\ +2 \\ \hline \end{array}$ **n** $\begin{array}{r} 1 \\ +6 \\ \hline \end{array}$ **o** $\begin{array}{r} 7 \\ +2 \\ \hline \end{array}$ **p** $\begin{array}{r} 6 \\ +4 \\ \hline \end{array}$

2 Adding coins

Finding totals of coins ( ).

Write the total of these coins.

Like this:  total is *7p*

3 Counting

Counting up to 10.

Count and write the number of squares on each t-shirt.

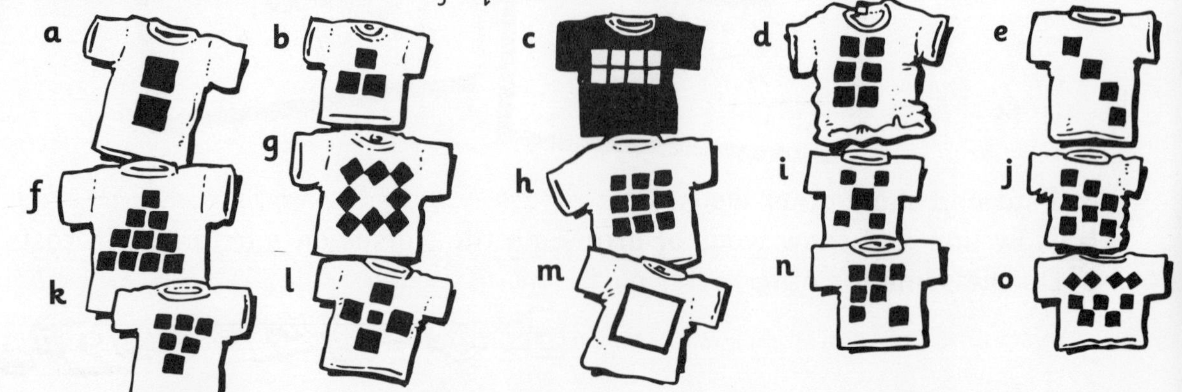

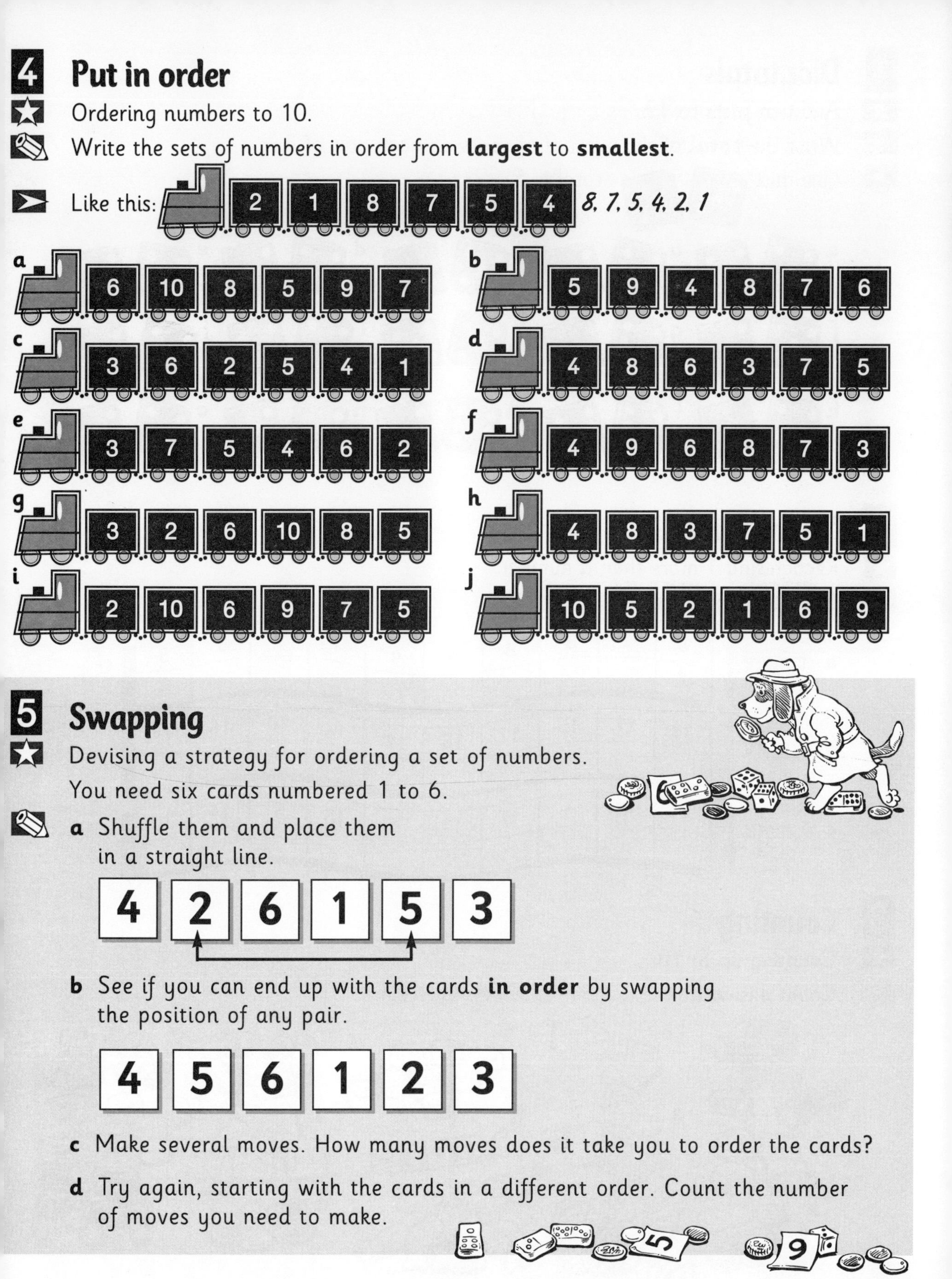

4 Put in order

Ordering numbers to 10.

Write the sets of numbers in order from **largest** to **smallest**.

Like this: 2 1 8 7 5 4 — *8, 7, 5, 4, 2, 1*

a 6 10 8 5 9 7

b 5 9 4 8 7 6

c 3 6 2 5 4 1

d 4 8 6 3 7 5

e 3 7 5 4 6 2

f 4 9 6 8 7 3

g 3 2 6 10 8 5

h 4 8 3 7 5 1

i 2 10 6 9 7 5

j 10 5 2 1 6 9

5 Swapping

Devising a strategy for ordering a set of numbers.

You need six cards numbered 1 to 6.

a Shuffle them and place them in a straight line.

4 2 6 1 5 3

b See if you can end up with the cards **in order** by swapping the position of any pair.

4 5 6 1 2 3

c Make several moves. How many moves does it take you to order the cards?

d Try again, starting with the cards in a different order. Count the number of moves you need to make.

1 Dice totals

Addition facts to 12.

Write the **total** of the number of spots on each pair of dice.

Like this: total is *5*.

a b c d e

f g h i j

k l m n o

2 'More' strips

Recognising 1 more than a number.

Copy and complete.

a 1 more

6	2	3	8	4	9	1	7	3	5
7									

b 1 more

13	17	15	11	18	19	14	10	16	12

c 1 more

7	13	4	17	11	6	15	3	14	9

3 Counting

Counting up to 10.

Count and write the number of sweets each time.

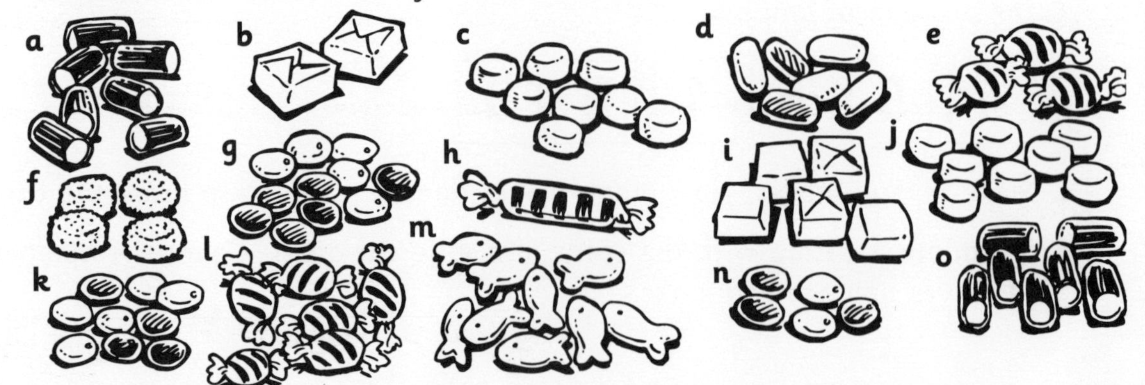

4 Put in order

Ordering numbers up to 20.

Write the sets of numbers in order from **smallest** to **largest**.

Like this: 7 11 19 14 8 4 *4, 7, 8, 11, 14, 19*

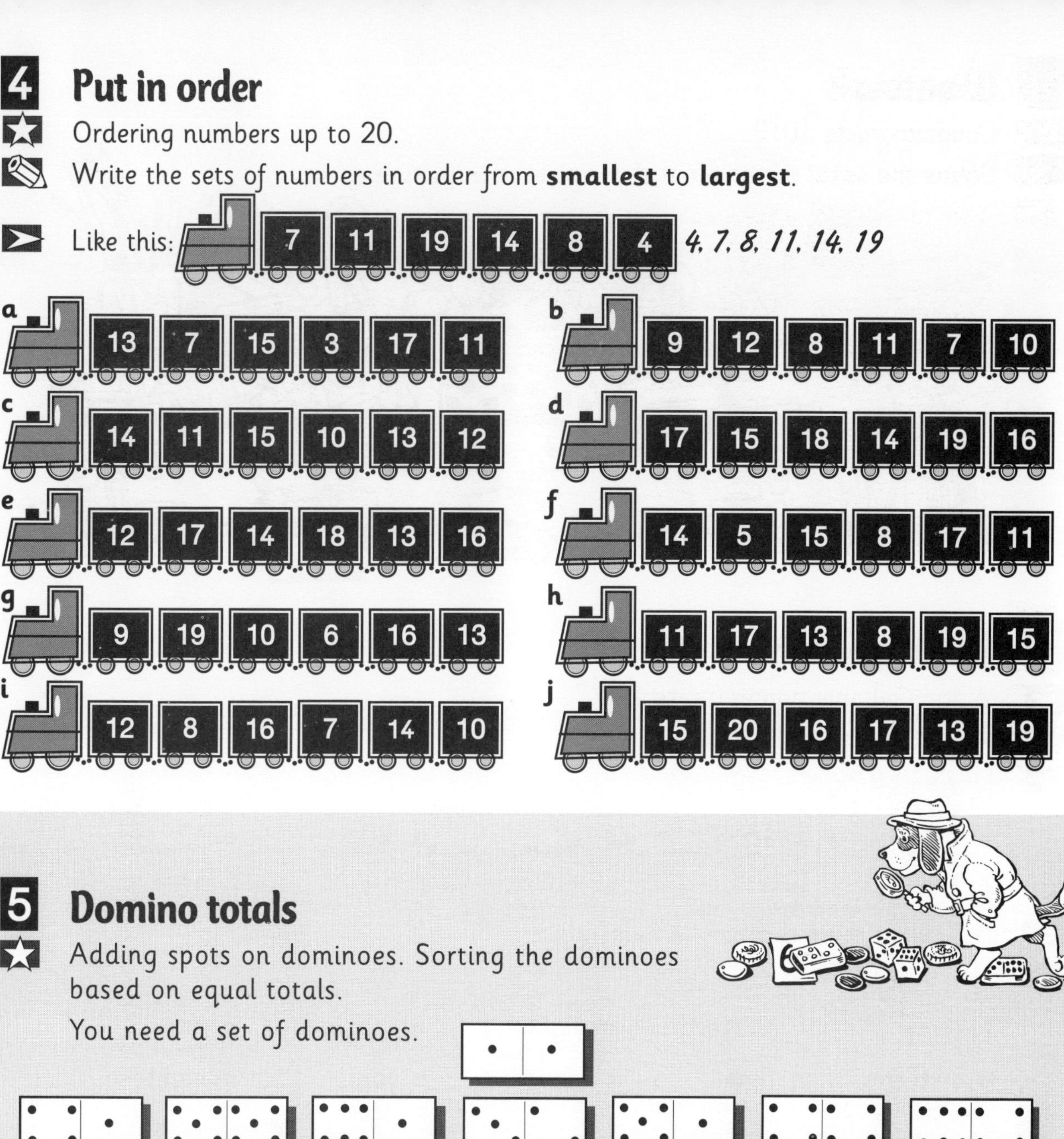

5 Domino totals

Adding spots on dominoes. Sorting the dominoes based on equal totals.

You need a set of dominoes.

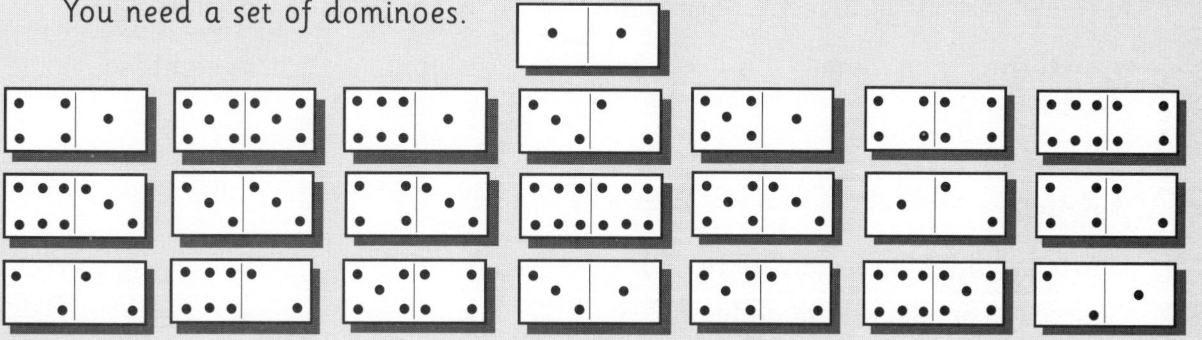

a Find and draw dominoes with a total of **9** spots.

b Do the same for other numbers of spots.

c Write **which total** has the most dominoes.

1 Counting

Counting up to 10.

Count and write the number of things in each picture.

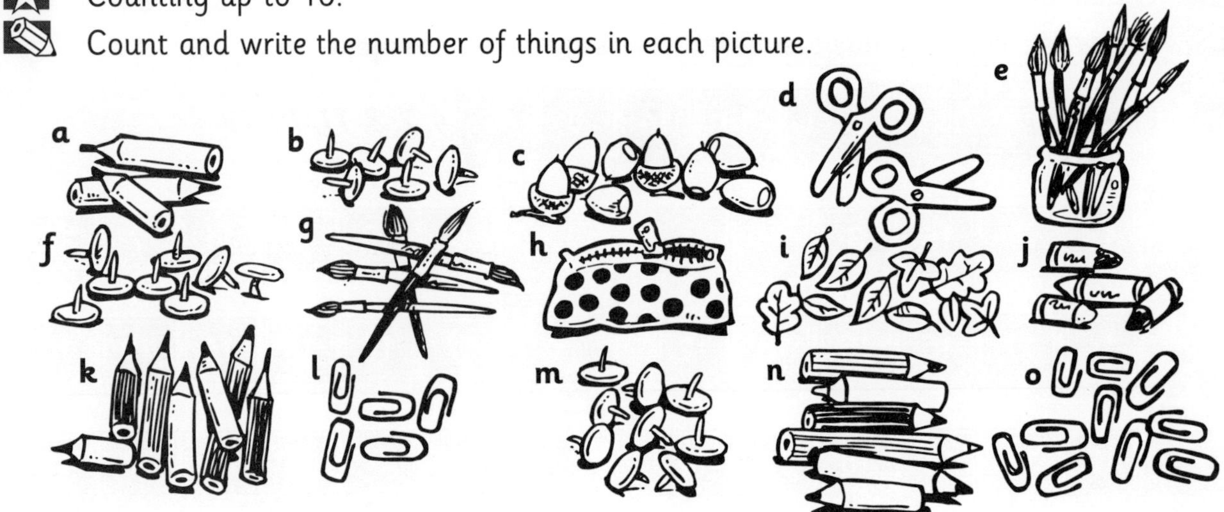

2 Writing number names

Writing number names (up to 20).

Write these numbers in words.

Like this: 8 *eight*

a 7 **b** 15 **c** 2 **d** 20 **e** 12

f 6 **g** 17 **h** 3 **i** 19 **j** 10

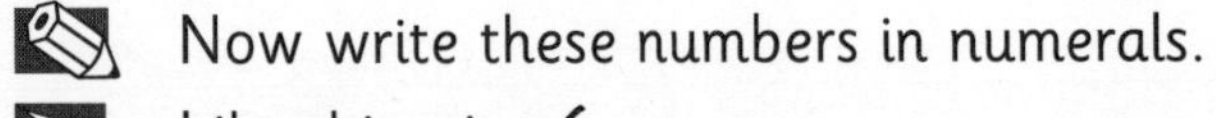

Now write these numbers in numerals.

Like this: six *6*

k five **l** thirteen **m** eight **n** fourteen **o** one

p sixteen **q** nine **r** eleven **s** four **t** eighteen

3 Adding

Horizontal addition (totals up to 10).

Copy and complete these additions.

Like this: *3+5=8*

a 1 + 2 **b** 2 + 4 **c** 3 + 7 **d** 6 + 2 **e** 3 + 1 **f** 7 + 1 **g** 3 + 3

h 2 + 1 **i** 1 + 4 **j** 4 + 2 **k** 1 + 5 **l** 4 + 3 **m** 8 + 2 **n** 2 + 5

o 3 + 4 **p** 3 + 5 **q** 2 + 7 **r** 5 + 5 **s** 1 + 8 **t** 5 + 3 **u** 4 + 4

4 Jumping addition

Adding facts up to 10.

Write the answers to these additions. Use the number line to help you.

Like this: 3 add 2 *5*

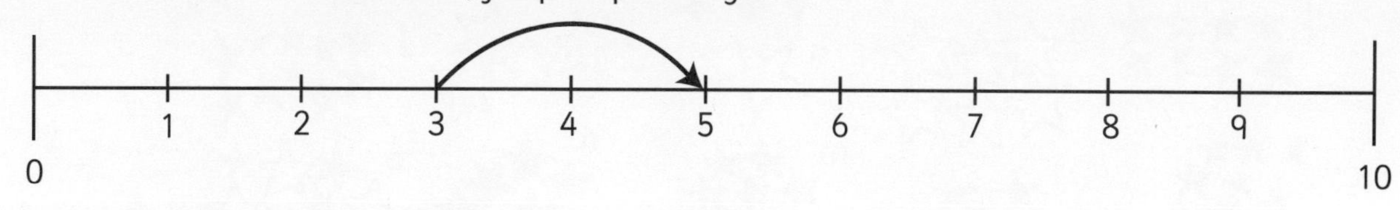

a 2 add 4	**b** 3 add 5	**c** 4 add 4	**d** 8 add 2	**e** 6 add 3
f 1 add 6	**g** 5 add 3	**h** 2 add 5	**i** 7 add 1	**j** 1 add 9
k 6 add 2	**l** 2 add 8	**m** 3 add 6	**n** 5 add 4	**o** 4 add 3
p 3 add 2	**q** 7 add 2	**r** 5 add 5	**s** 4 add 1	**t** 8 add 1

5 Writing numbers

Writing and counting the number of letters in number names to 20.
Sorting the words according to number of letters.

a Investigate the number of letters in numbers from 1 to 20.
Write your answers each time.

Like this:

The number **7** has five letters. — 1 2 3 4 5 / *7 seven*

The number **13** has eight letters. — 1 2 3 4 5 6 7 8 / *13 thirteen*

b Which has the **most** letters? Which has the **fewest**?
c Which have the **same** number of letters?

1 Counting

Counting up to 11.

Count and write the number of stars in each picture.

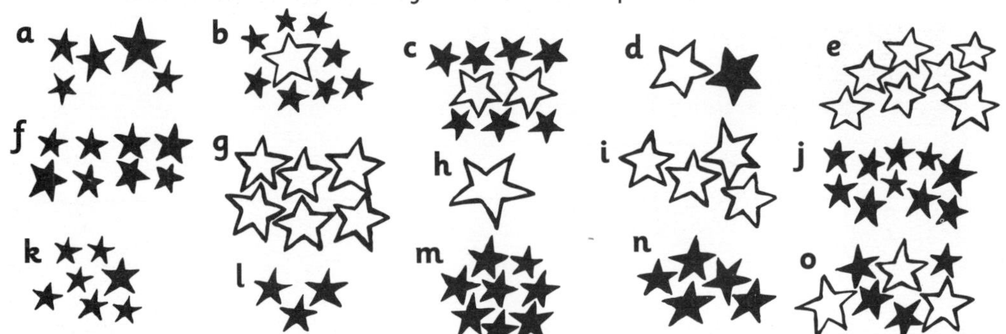

2 'Less' strips

Recognising 1 less than a number (up to 20).

Copy and complete.

a 1 less

8	2	5	10	3	7	1	4	9	6
7									

b 1 less

17	12	10	19	15	20	13	16	18	14

c 1 less

7	15	10	17	19	12	9	13	20	8

3 Put in order

Ordering numbers up to 20.

Write the sets of numbers in order from **smallest** to **largest**.

Like this: 14 9 5 18 11 2 *2, 5, 9, 11, 14, 18*

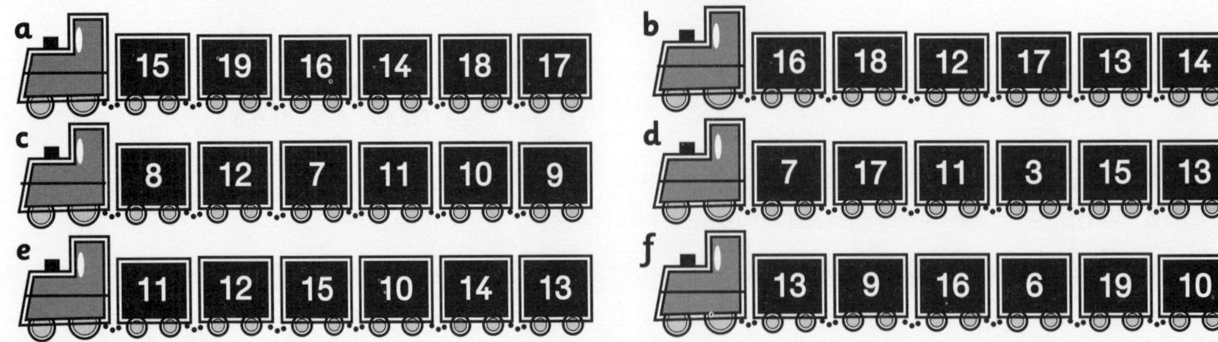

4 Ordering

Ordering a set of 2-digit numbers.

Write the numbers in each set in order, from **smallest** to **largest**.

Like this: 62 45 57 34 73 26 — *26, 34, 45, 57, 62, 73*

a 23 27 24 / 28 26 29	**b** 35 36 31 / 38 33 37	**c** 65 69 64 / 67 61 63	**d** 86 80 89 / 82 85 84
e 41 46 44 / 43 48 40	**f** 63 41 27 / 15 36 52	**g** 84 34 91 / 42 60 59	**h** 18 39 27 / 62 51 46

Write the numbers in each set in order, from **largest** to **smallest**.

i 57 53 58 / 55 59 51	**j** 92 98 93 / 95 94 96	**k** 73 76 79 / 71 78 72	**l** 16 19 13 / 18 17 11
m 46 24 63 / 19 35 54	**n** 72 65 81 / 54 99 43	**o** 38 36 42 / 31 39 50	**p** 52 43 63 / 45 57 72

5 Coins

Making a given sum of money using different numbers of coins.

Use 

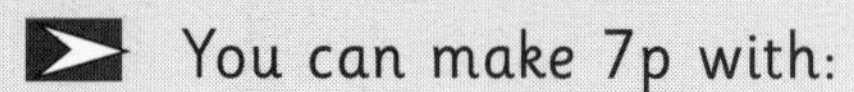

You can make 7p with:

2 coins 

5 coins 

3 coins 

6 coins 

4 coins 

7 coins 

a Investigate different ways of making **6p**. Show your answers.

b Investigate different ways of making **other** amounts.

1 Numbers to 10

Recognising number bonds up to 10.

There are 10 squares in each strip.

Count how many are ■ shaded □ not shaded.

Like this:  *4 and 6*

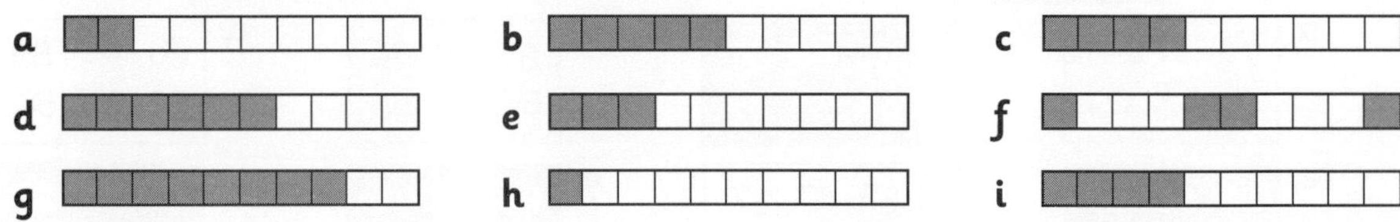

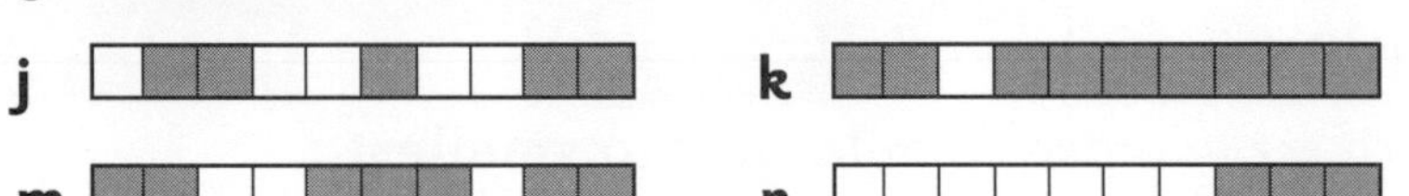

a b c d e f g h i j k l m n o

2 Writing number names

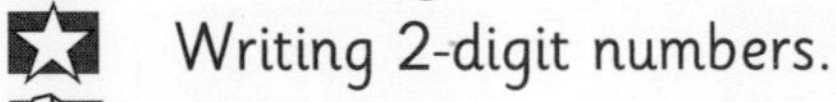

Writing 2-digit numbers.

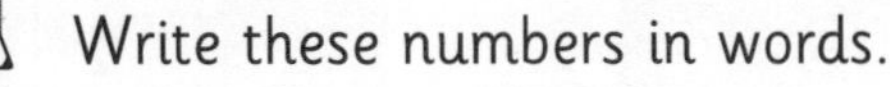

Write these numbers in words.

Like this: 54 *fifty-four*

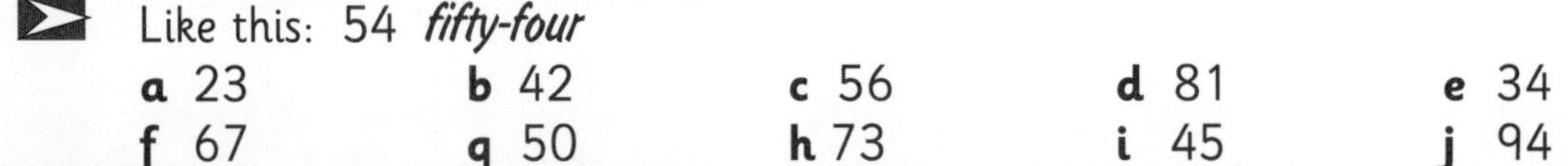

a 23 **b** 42 **c** 56 **d** 81 **e** 34
f 67 **g** 50 **h** 73 **i** 45 **j** 94

Now write these numbers in numerals.

Like this: twenty-five *25*

k eighteen **l** seventy-five **m** thirty-five **n** eighty-four **o** forty-three
p ninety-seven **q** fifty-eight **r** twenty-six **s** sixty-four **t** thirty-one

3 Jumping subtraction

Subtraction from 10.

Write the answers to these subtractions. Use the number line to help you.

Like this: 6 take away 2 *4*

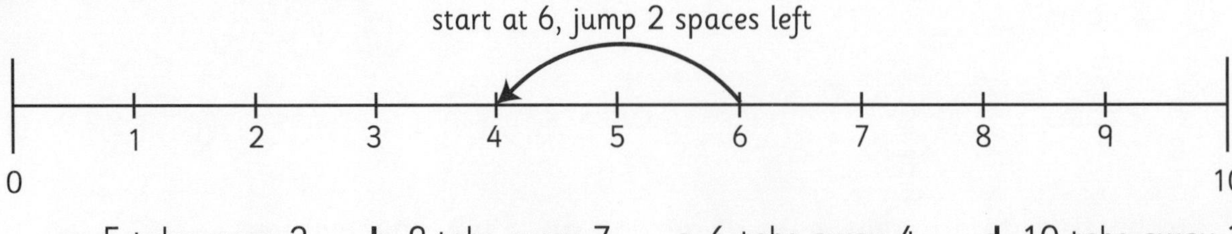

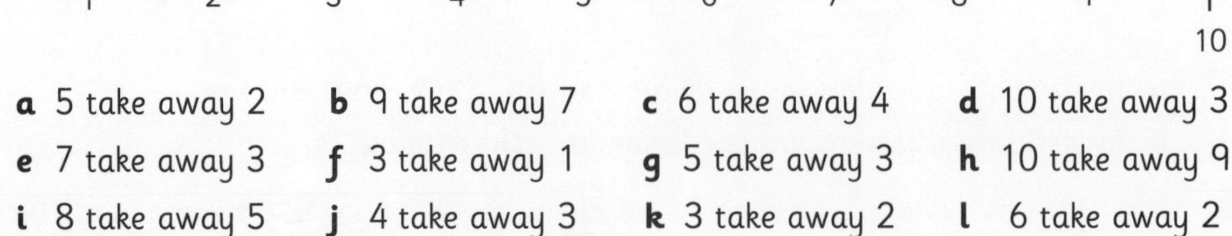

a 5 take away 2 **b** 9 take away 7 **c** 6 take away 4 **d** 10 take away 3
e 7 take away 3 **f** 3 take away 1 **g** 5 take away 3 **h** 10 take away 9
i 8 take away 5 **j** 4 take away 3 **k** 3 take away 2 **l** 6 take away 2

4 Card totals

Addition facts up to 10.

Write the **total** of the numbers on each pair of cards.

Like this: 2 4 total *6*

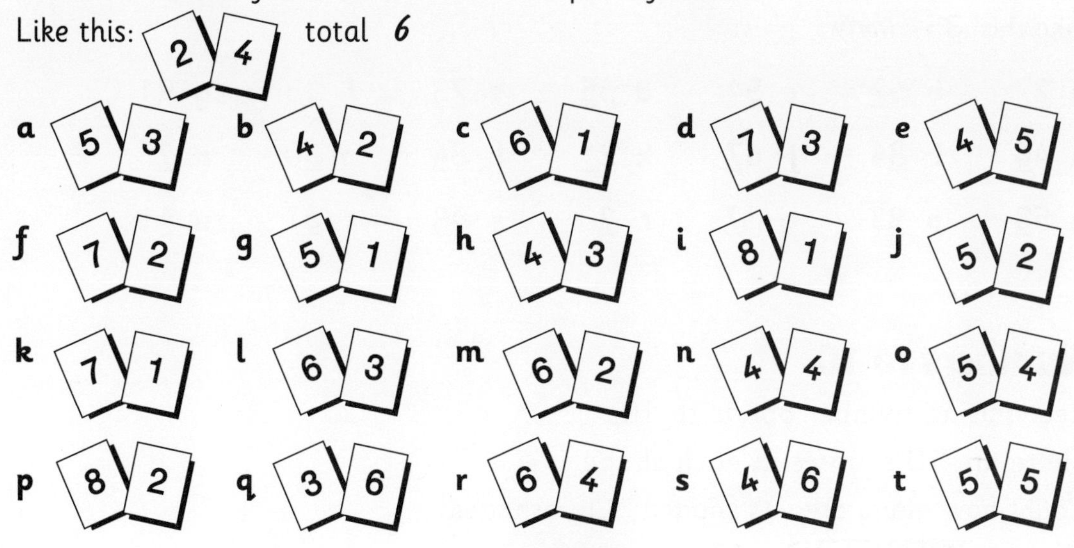

5 Making 4

Investigating different additions with the same total.

Use **adding** only.

Here are different ways of making 4.

1 + 1 + 1 + 1
1 + 1 + 2
1 + 3
2 + 2

→ **4 ways altogether**

a Find and write different ways of making **5**.

b Try different ways of making other numbers. Write your answers.

1 Place value

Recognising the place value of digits in 2-digit numbers.

Write the value of the **bold** numeral.

Like this: **3**5 *thirty*

a **2**7 **b** 6**2** **c** **5**4 **d** 3**5** **e** **7**3 **f** **1**3 **g** 9**1**

h 4**6** **i** **8**4 **j** 6**7** **k** 2**1** **l** 8**4** **m** **3**0 **n** **7**5

o 5**8** **p** **9**3 **q** 1**7** **r** **2**0 **s** 4**9** **t** **6**7 **u** **4**1

2 Numbers to 10

Recognising number bonds to 10.

There are 10 squares in each shape.

Count how many are: ■ shaded □ unshaded.

Like this: 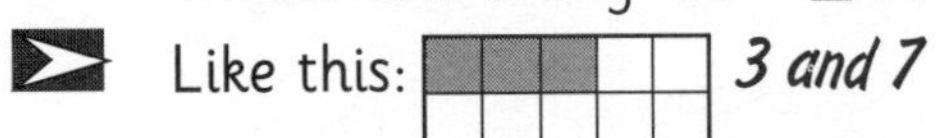

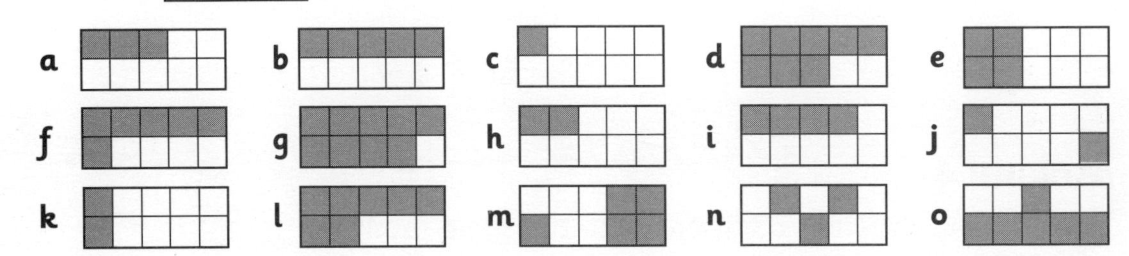

3 Sequences

Finding missing entries in a number sequence (steps of 3, 4).

Write the missing numbers in each sequence.

Like this:

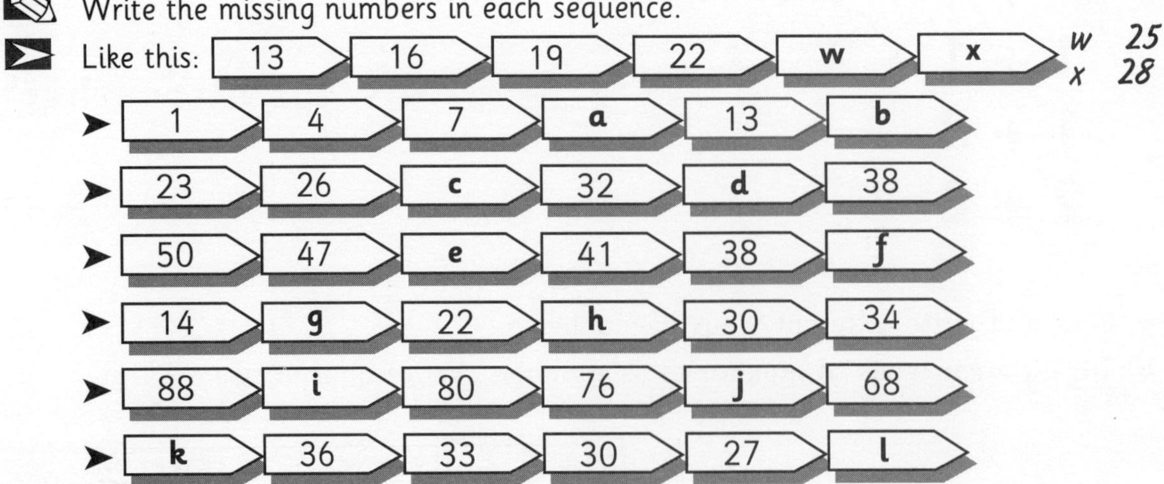

4 Pictograph

Interpreting a pictograph, in which 1 picture represents 1 unit.

Use the pictograph to help you answer the questions.

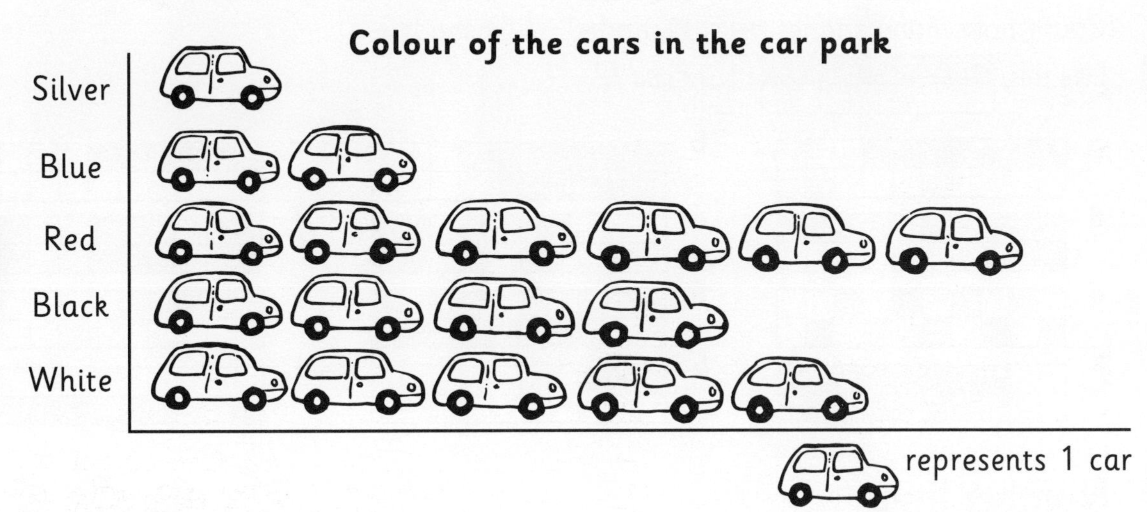

a Which colour is **most** common?

b Which colour is **least** common?

How many cars are: **c** black **d** blue **e** white **f** silver **g** red?

h How many **more** are red than blue?

i How many **more** are black than silver?

j How many **more** are white than black?

k How many **more** are blue than silver?

l How many **fewer** are blue than black?

m How many **fewer** are silver than white?

n How many cars **altogether**?

o How many cars are **not blue**?

5 Adding

Investigating addition bonds to 10, and other numbers.

Add any 2 numbers. Use numbered cards if it helps.

The total must be **10** each time.

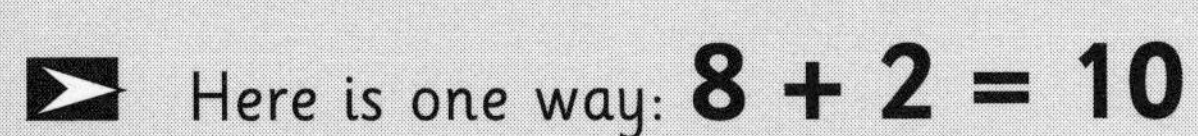

Here is one way: **8 + 2 = 10**

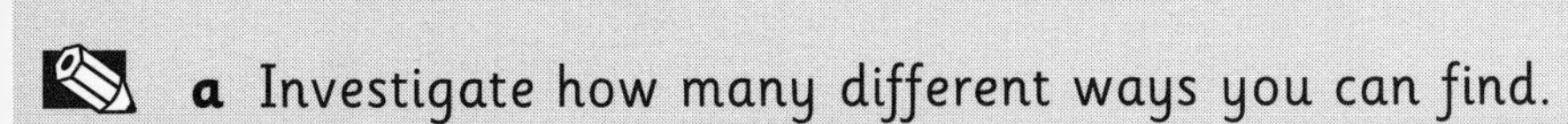

a Investigate how many different ways you can find.

b Find different ways of making a total of **12**.

c Do the same for your own totals.

1 Numbers to 20

Recognising number bonds up to 20.

There are 20 squares in each shape.

Count how many shapes are ■shaded □unshaded.

Like this: 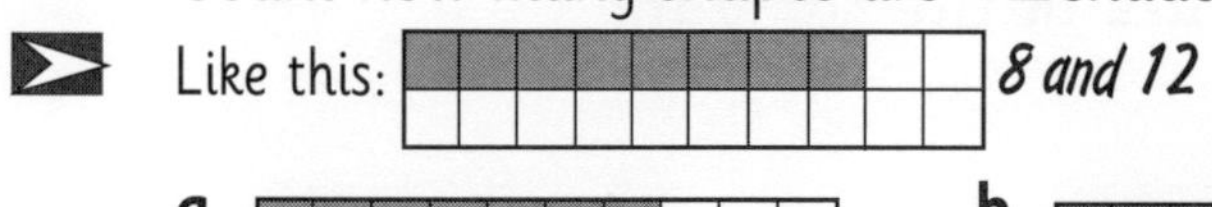 *8 and 12*

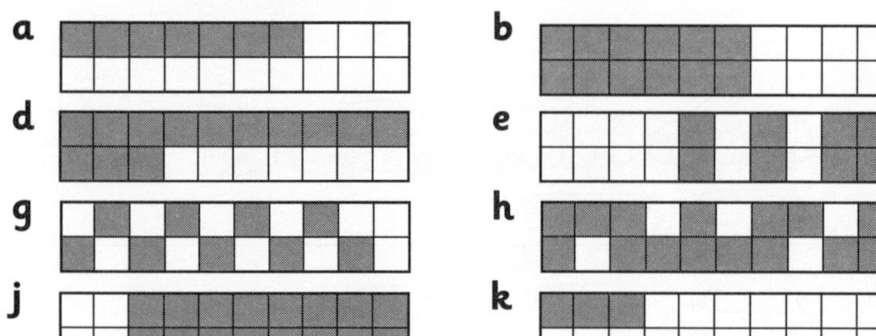

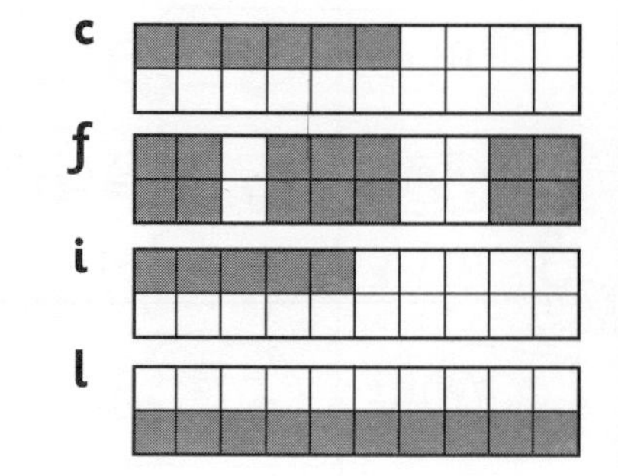

2 Number lines

Finding points on a number line marked in ones.

Write the position of each letter on the lines.

Like this: **a** *12*

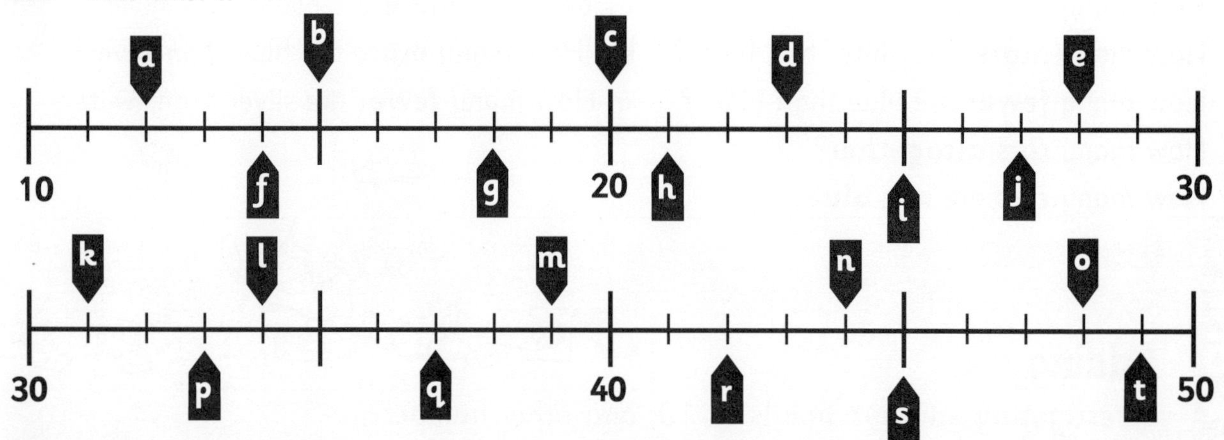

3 'More' strips

Recognising 2 more and 3 more than a number (up to 10).

Copy and complete.

a 2 more

b 3 more

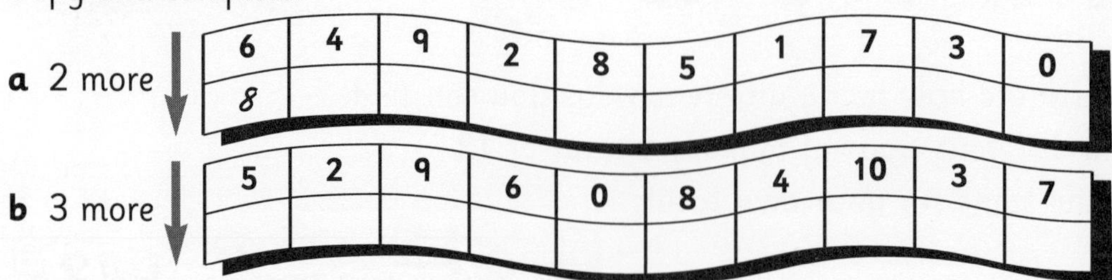

4 Prices

Choosing coins to make an exact amount.

Use these coins.

Write **2** coins which make these prices exactly.

Like this:

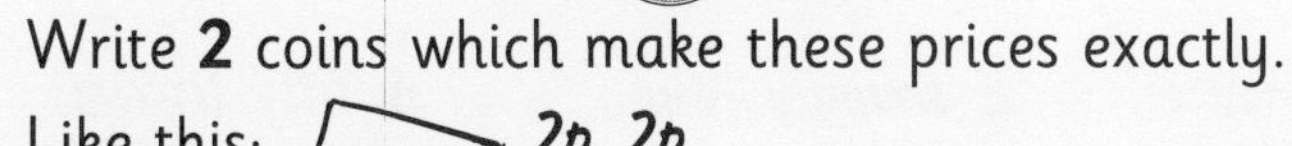

Write **3** coins which make these prices exactly.

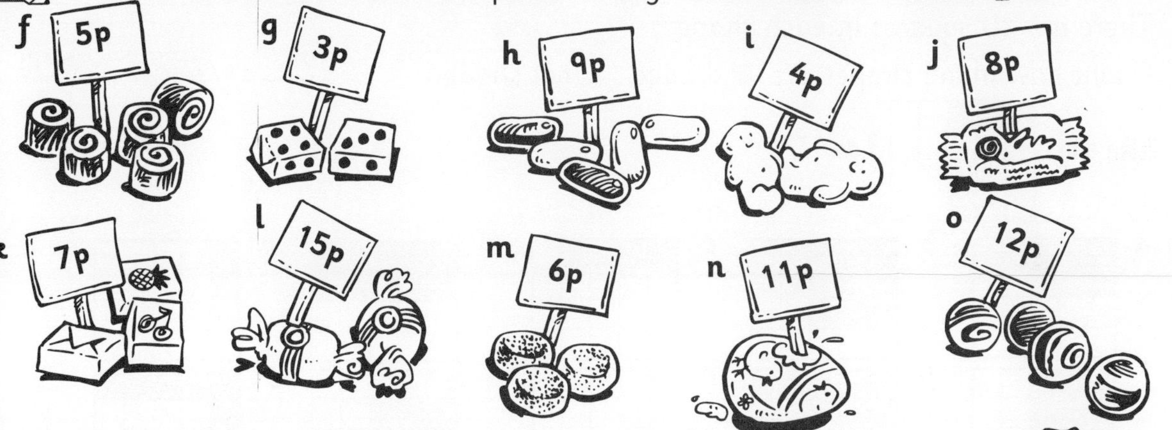

5 Dice sums

Adding the number of spots on two dice.
Investigating different possible totals. You need two dice.

Here are 3 different ways of making a total of **6**.

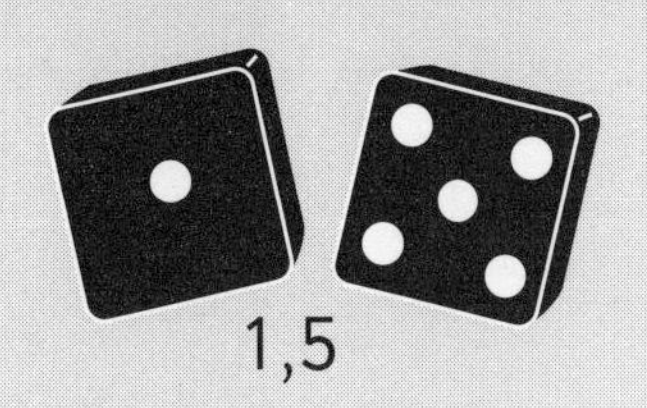

1,5

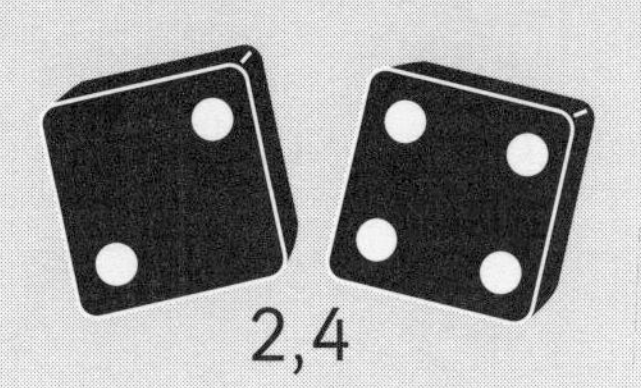

2,4

3,3

a Investigate and show different ways of making a total of **7**.

b Find more ways of making different totals.

1 Writing numerals

Writing 2-digit number names in numerals.

Write these number names in numerals.

Like this: fifty-two *52*

a **forty-eight**	b twenty-nine	c ***seventy-four***	d *fifty-three*
e twelve	f **eighty-seven**	g thirty-five	h ninety-three
i *forty*	j *sixty-six*	k **fifty-five**	l thirty-one

2 Numbers to 20

Recognising number bonds up to 20.

There are 20 squares in each shape.

Count how many shapes are ■ shaded □ not shaded.

Like this: *3 and 17*

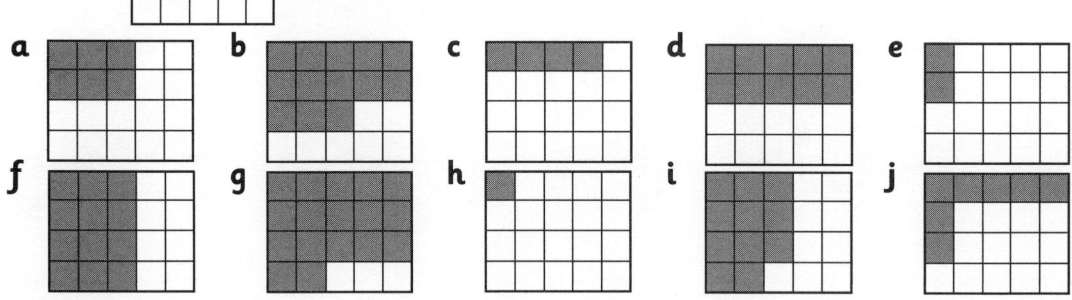

3 Darts

Adding two numbers (totals up to 10).

Write the total score for these pairs of darts of the same colour.

Like this: **a** *2+7=9*

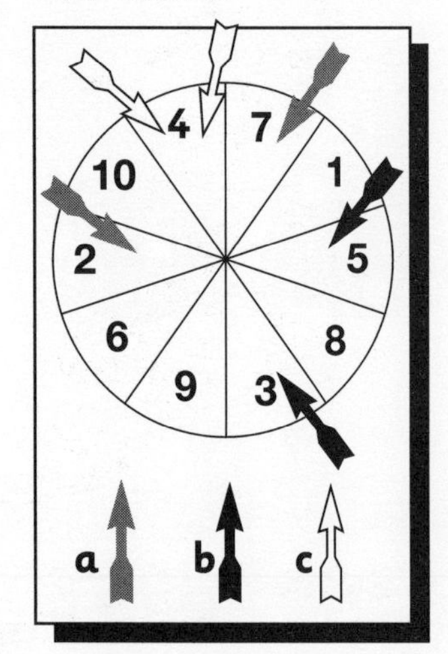

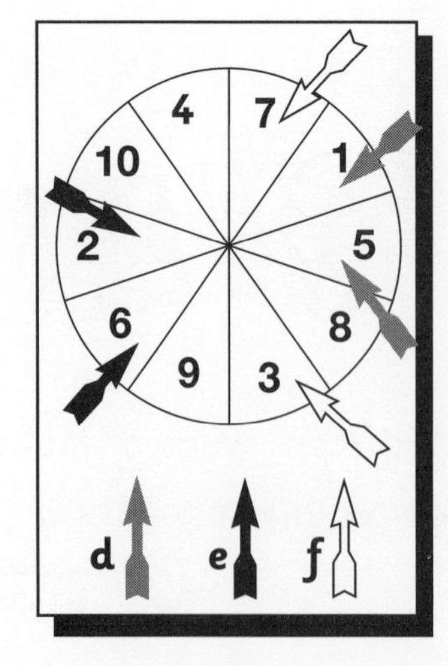

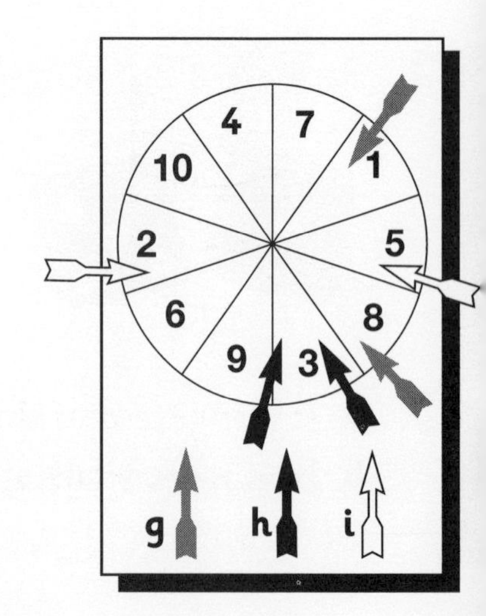

4 Choosing numbers

Vertical addition (totals up to 10).

Choose two of the numbers to make the additions work. Write your additions.

Like this:

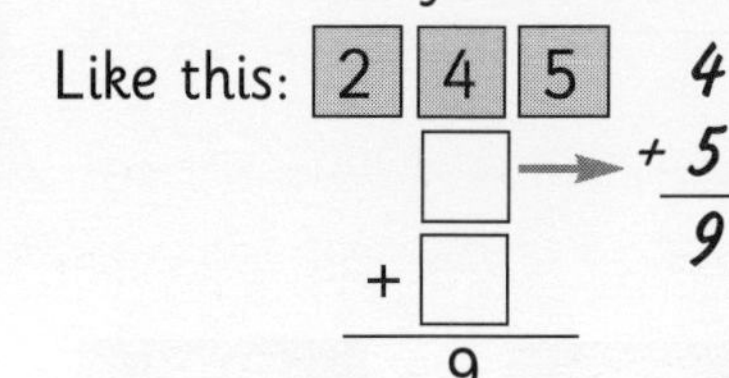

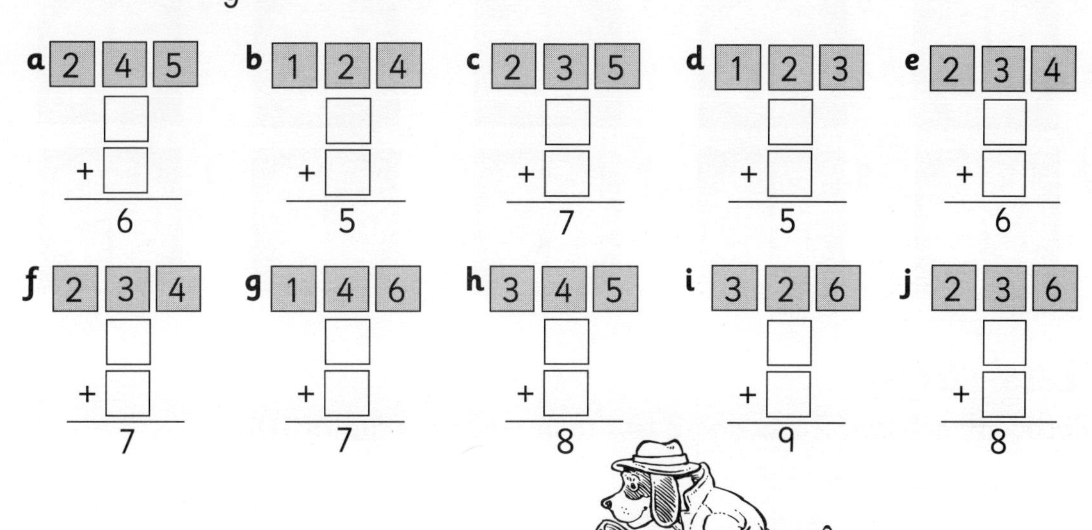

5 3 piles

Investigating ways of splitting a set of eight into three.

You need 8 counters.

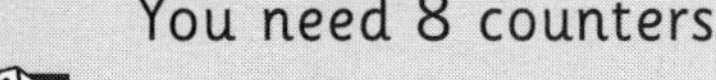

a Make three piles. Write the number of counters in each pile.

Here is one way of doing it.

b How many different **ways** can you find? Write your answers.

c In how many ways can you make **2** piles of the 8 counters?

1 Clocks

Reading an analogue clock (o'clocks, half past).

Write the time shown on these clocks.

Like this:  *3 o'clock*

a 
b
c 
d 
e 

f 
g 
h 
i 
j 

2 'Less' strips

Recognising 1 less, 2 less and 3 less than a number (up to 10).

Copy and complete.

a 1 less

4	6	9	7	2	5	8	1	10	3
3									

b 2 less

4	7	2	9	6	10	5	8	11	3

c 3 less

6	10	4	8	12	3	7	11	5	9

3 Place value

Recognising the place-value of digits in 2-digit numbers.

Write the value of the **bold** numeral.

Like this: **5**2 *fifty*

a **7**8 **b** 8**4** **c** **6**8 **d** **3**0 **e** 1**6**

f **7**3 **g** 2**7** **h** **9**1 **i** **4**5 **j** 5**9**

k 1**2** **l** **6**4 **m** **2**8 **n** 8**1** **o** 5**7**

p **9**3 **q** 3**5** **r** **7**0 **s** 4**6** **t** **6**9

4 Stamps

Adding two sums of money (totals up to 14p).

Here are 5 different stamps.

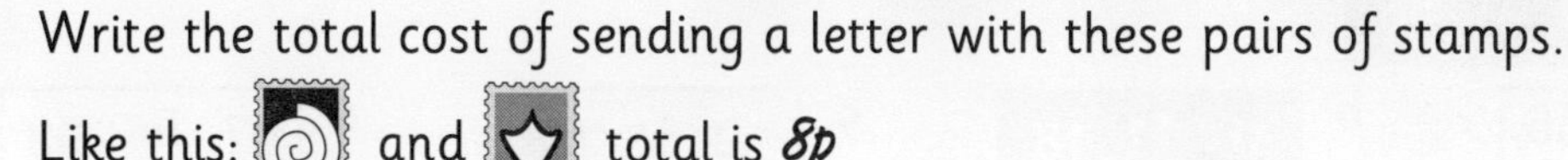

Write the total cost of sending a letter with these pairs of stamps.

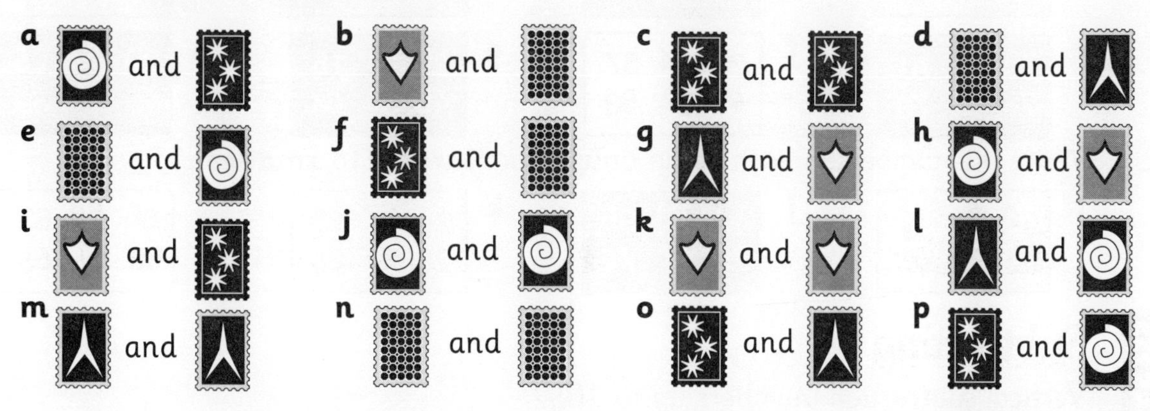

5 Card sums

Adding 1-digit numbers. Investigating different additions based on a fixed set of digits.

You need cards numbered from 1 to 9.

a Place **three** cards to make an addition. Then write it.

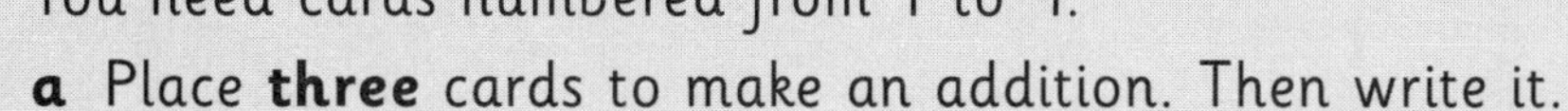

Like this:

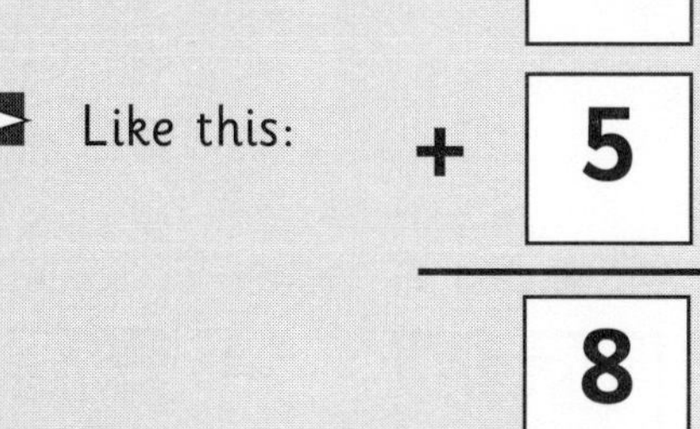

b Investigate how many different additions you can make. Write your additions each time.

1 Ordering

Ordering a set of 2-digit numbers.

Write the numbers in each set in order, from **smallest** to **largest**.

Like this: 38 80 43 29 91 55 *29, 38, 43, 55, 80, 91*

a 31 39 36 30 38 33

b 16 11 18 13 12 17

c 59 55 57 52 58 53

d 97 94 93 95 98 90

e 73 75 70 76 79 78

f 35 24 37 41 52 63

g 29 51 18 49 38 64

h 29 37 25 45 14 39

Write the numbers in each set in order, from **largest** to **smallest**.

i 79 64 72 55 83 68

j 81 89 95 79 97 74

k 24 27 23 26 25 28

l 66 68 63 69 67 65

2 Subtracting

Vertical subtraction (numbers up to 10).

Copy and complete these subtractions.

Like this: *7 - 2 = 5*

a 4 - 2	**b** 9 - 3	**c** 5 - 1	**d** 8 - 1	**e** 10 - 4	**f** 10 - 2	**g** 3 - 1	**h** 10 - 1
i 8 - 3	**j** 9 - 5	**k** 6 - 4	**l** 10 - 3	**m** 7 - 5	**n** 7 - 2	**o** 5 - 4	**p** 8 - 5

3 Clocks

Reading a digital clock (o'clocks, half past).

Write the time shown on these clocks.

Like this: 06:30 *half past 6*

a 03:00	**b** 01:30	**c** 05:30	**d** 08:30	**e** 01:00
f 11:30	**g** 02:00	**h** 10:00	**i** 04:00	**j** 06:00
k 06:30	**l** 02:30	**m** 11:00	**n** 05:00	**o** 09:00

4 Writing numerals

Writing 2-digit numerals.

Write the number shown by the beads on each abacus.

Like this: *27*

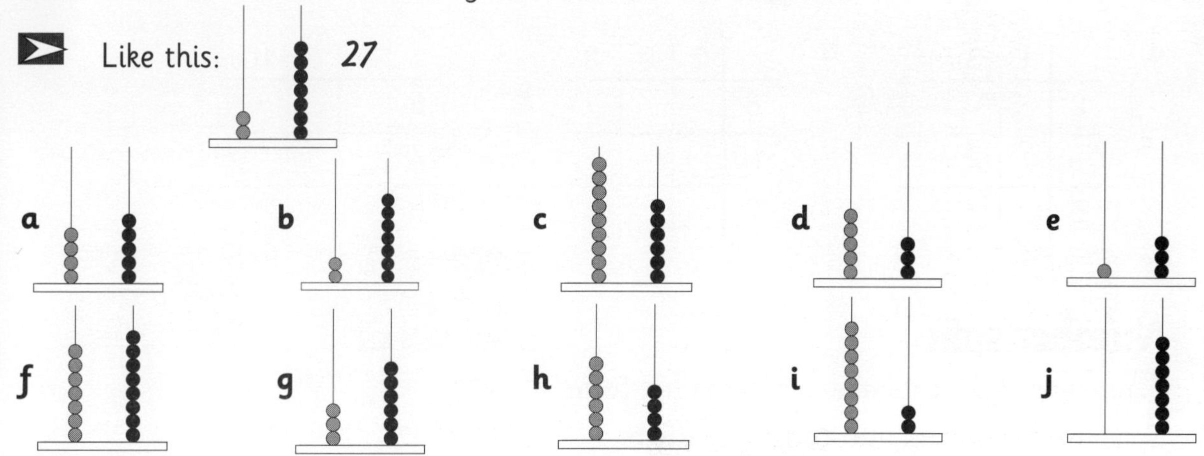

Now draw an abacus to show each of these numbers.

k 39 **l** 25 **m** 40 **n** 18 **o** 9

5 Dice differences

Finding the difference between two numbers. Investigating different arrangements to make a given difference (numbers to 6).

You need two dice.

Here are three ways of making a difference of **3**.

3,6

2,5

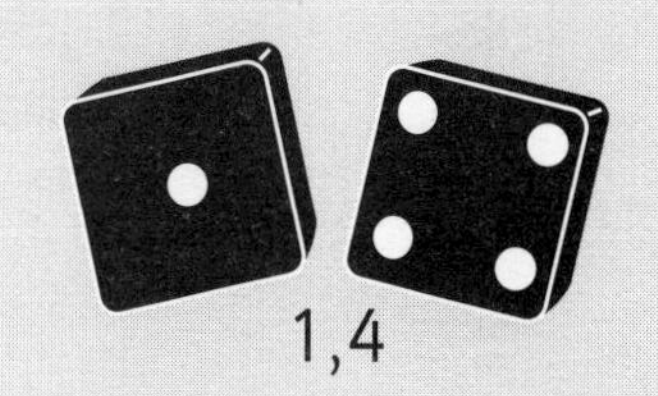

1,4

a Investigate different ways of making a difference of **2**. Show your answers.

b Find other ways of making more differences.

1 Difference tables

Finding the difference between two numbers (up to 10).

Copy and complete these **difference** tables.

a

	1	3	4
2			
5		*2*	
6			

b

	7	9	3
8			
10			
2			

c

	7	6	10
5			
4			
8			

2 Number split

Expressing 2-digit numbers in extended form.

Split these numbers into **tens** and **units**.

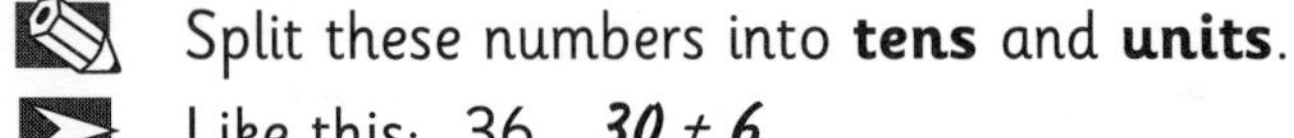

Like this: 36 *30 + 6*

a 49 **b** 84 **c** 28 **d** 73 **e** 17

f 51 **g** 36 **h** 60 **i** 95 **j** 42

k 53 **l** 15 **m** 31 **n** 27 **o** 70

p 48 **q** 82 **r** 66 **s** 94 **t** 59

3 Fewest coins

Choosing the fewest coins to make given amounts.

Use 1p, 2p, 5p coins.

Write the **fewest** coins needed to buy these shapes.

Like this: 11p 3 coins: *5p, 5p, 1p*

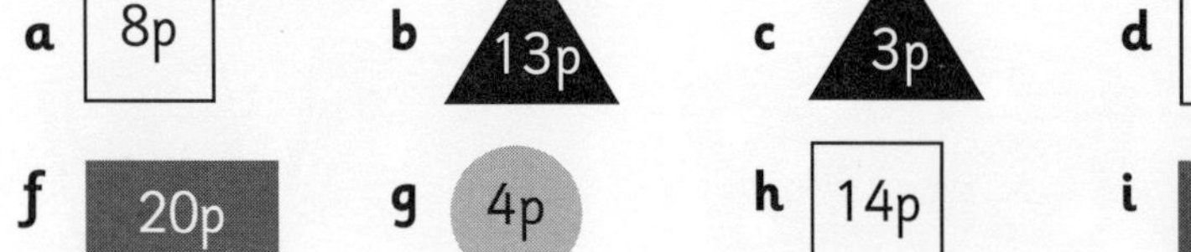

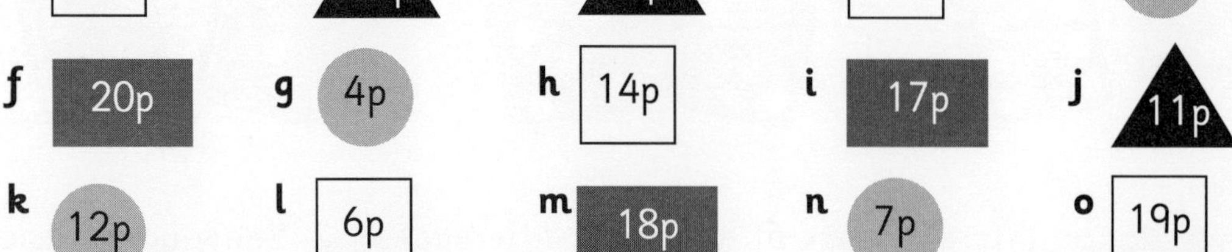

a 8p **b** 13p **c** 3p **d** 15p **e** 9p

f 20p **g** 4p **h** 14p **i** 17p **j** 11p

k 12p **l** 6p **m** 18p **n** 7p **o** 19p

p 25p **q** 10p **r** 16p **s** 22p **t** 21p

4 'More' strips

Recognising 1 more, 2 more and 3 more than a number (up to 20).

Copy and complete.

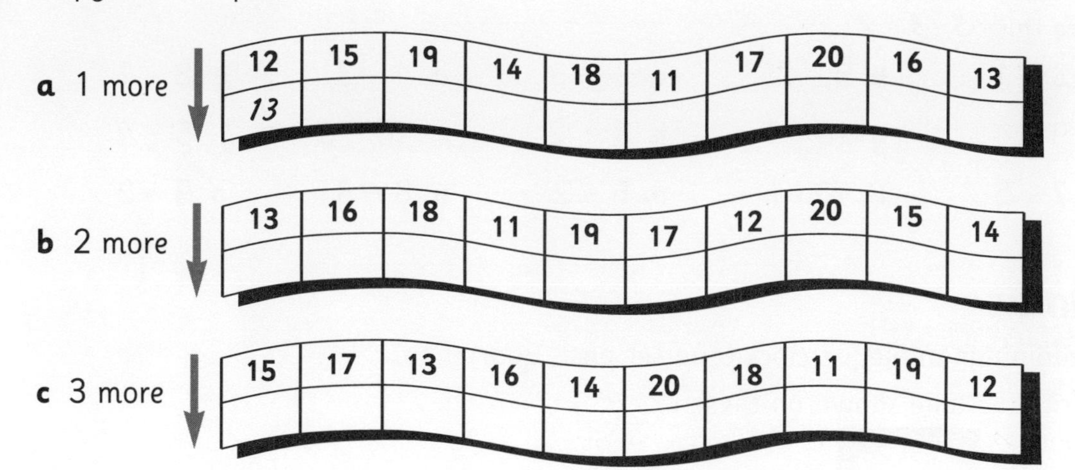

5 Different additions

Adding two 1-digit numbers. Investigating different possible totals when choosing two numbers from five.

Use five cards numbered like this. **3** **4** **5** **6** **7**

Make an addition by choosing **two** of the cards. What is the total?

Like this: **3** + **6** = *9*

a Investigate **all** the different possible totals when choosing two cards. Write your addition and total each time.

1 Subtracting

Horizontal subtraction (numbers up to 10).

Copy and complete these subtractions.

Like this: *5 - 3 = 2*

a 3 – 1	**b** 5 – 2	**c** 7 – 3	**d** 4 – 3	**e** 8 – 1
f 9 – 4	**g** 10 – 3	**h** 3 – 2	**i** 10 – 5	**j** 5 – 4
k 7 – 5	**l** 10 – 1	**m** 6 – 2	**n** 8 – 3	**o** 9 – 2

2 Clocks

Reading an analogue clock (quarter past, quarter to).

Write the time shown on these clocks.

Like this:  *quarter past 3*

a 
b 
c 
d 
e 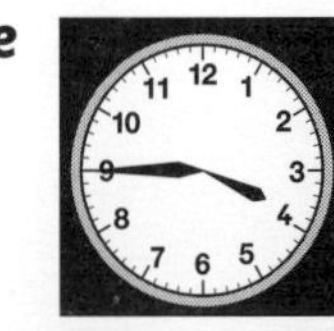

f 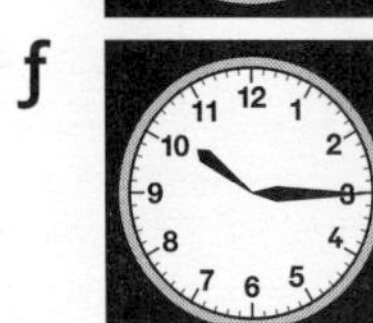
g 
h 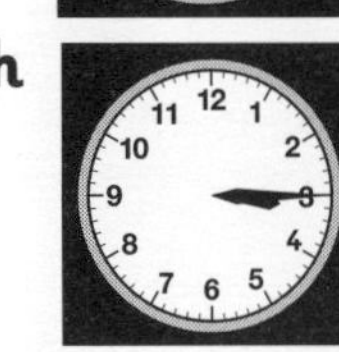
i 
j 

3 Sequences

Finding missing entries in a number sequence (steps of 5, 10).

Write the missing numbers in each sequence.

Like this: 15 ➤ 20 ➤ **w** ➤ 30 ➤ 35 ➤ **x** ➤ *w 25* *x 40*

➤ 5 ➤ 10 ➤ **a** ➤ 20 ➤ 25 ➤ **b** ➤

➤ 45 ➤ **c** ➤ 35 ➤ 30 ➤ **d** ➤ 20 ➤

➤ **e** ➤ 65 ➤ 70 ➤ 75 ➤ 80 ➤ **f** ➤

➤ 10 ➤ 20 ➤ **g** ➤ 40 ➤ 50 ➤ **h** ➤

➤ 75 ➤ **i** ➤ 65 ➤ **j** ➤ 55 ➤ 50 ➤

4 Gaps

Writing 2-digit numbers in words.

Write the missing words.

Like this: 73 seventy-...... *three*

a	46 forty-...........	b	62 sixty-...........	c	23 ....-three
d	81 ....-one	e	28 twenty-...........	f	73 seventy-...........
g	34 thirty-..............	h	58 ....-eight	i	94 ninety-...........
j	68 ....-eight	k	63 sixty-...........	l	38 ....-eight
m	86 ....-six	n	45 forty-...........	o	75 ....-five
p	27 twenty-.........	q	82 ....-two	r	51 ....-one
s	92 ninety-...........	t	66 sixty-...........	u	42 ...... -two

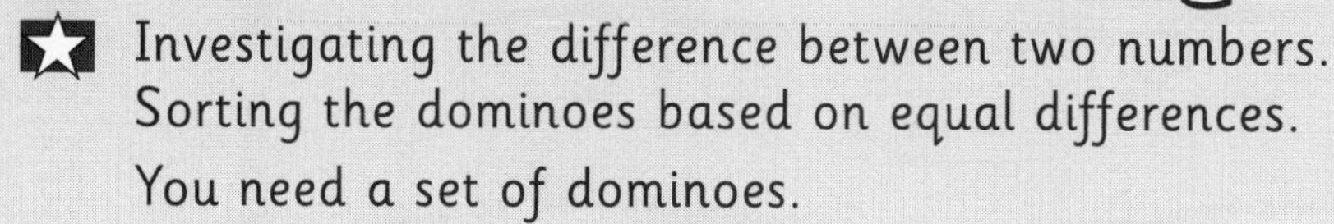

5 Domino differences

Investigating the difference between two numbers.
Sorting the dominoes based on equal differences.

You need a set of dominoes.

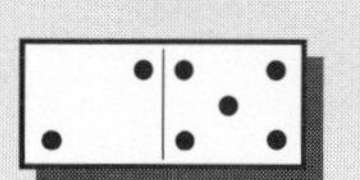

The difference between the spots on each side of this domino is 3.

Like this: *5 - 2 = 3*

a Find and draw other dominoes with a difference of **3**. How many are there?

b How many can you find with a difference of **2**. Draw them.

c Investigate dominoes for **other** differences.

d What is the **most common** difference?

e What is the **least common** difference?

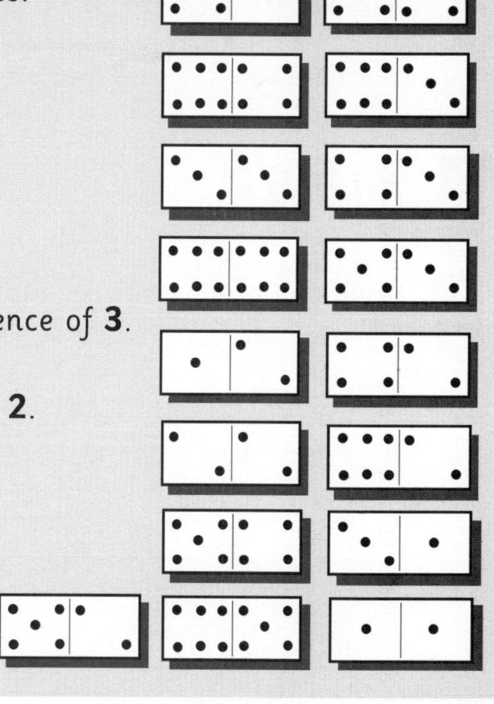

1 What's the number?

Recognising the value of numbers written in extended form.

Write the value of these numbers.

Like this: 20 + 7 *27*

a 40 + 2	**b** 10 + 6	**c** 30 + 8	**d** 80 + 1	**e** 20 + 5
f 70 + 3	**g** 50 + 9	**h** 90 + 4	**i** 7 + 60	**j** 40 + 2
k 10 + 4	**l** 1 + 90	**m** 50 + 7	**n** 2 + 80	**o** 6 + 20
p 9 + 70	**q** 40 + 3	**r** 30 + 6	**s** 8 + 60	**t** 7 + 30

2 Strips of pairs

Finding pairs of numbers to make 10.

Copy the strips. Write numbers in the bottom row.

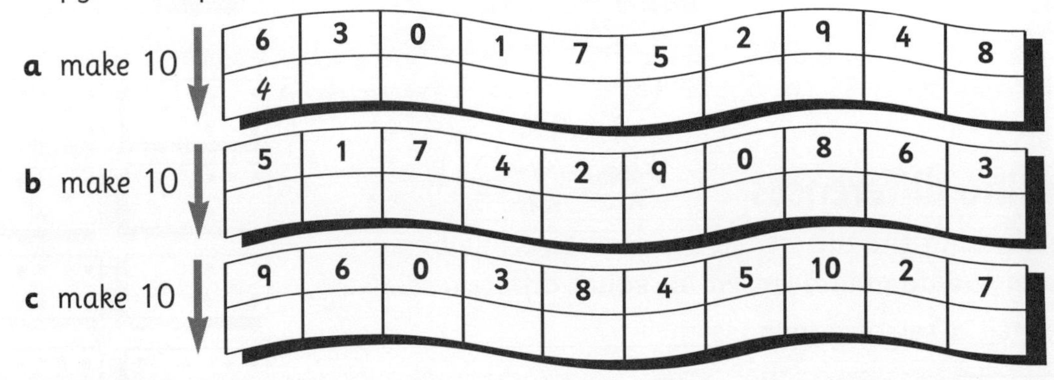

3 Adding

Vertical addition (totals up to 20).

Copy and complete these additions.

Like this: *8 + 7 = 15*

a 3 + 8 **b** 4 + 9 **c** 14 + 3 **d** 7 + 6 **e** 12 + 5 **f** 9 + 7 **g** 17 + 2 **h** 1 + 9

i 5 + 14 **j** 18 + 1 **k** 8 + 8 **l** 13 + 4 **m** 11 + 5 **n** 10 + 6 **o** 15 + 3 **p** 6 + 12

4 Jumping forwards and backwards

Addition and subtraction facts to 20.

Write the answers to these additions and subtractions.

Use the number line to help you.

Like this: 11 take away 4 *7*

11 add 4 *15*

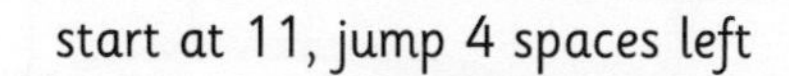

start at 11, jump 4 spaces right

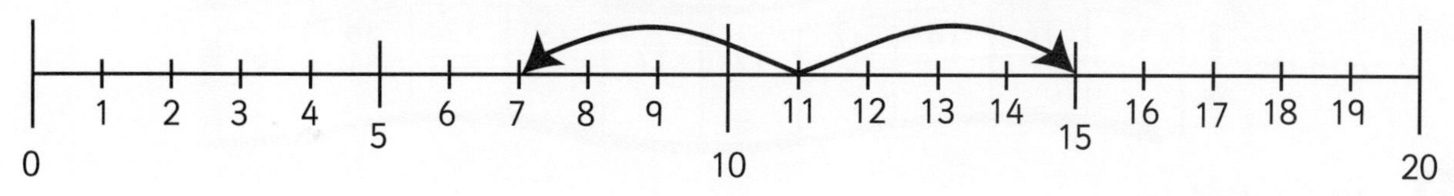

a 2 add 5 **b** 8 take away 6 **c** 3 add 6 **d** 4 add 4

e 7 take away 1 **f** 10 take away 3 **g** 3 add 2 **h** 6 take away 4

i 9 take away 5 **j** 5 take away 2 **k** 1 add 8 **l** 2 add 7

m 10 take away 8 **n** 5 add 3 **o** 8 take away 3 **p** 8 add 1

q 6 add 2 **r** 7 take away 5 **s** 9 take away 2 **t** 7 add 2

5 Writing numbers

Writing and counting the number of letters in 2-digit numbers.
Sorting the words according to number of letters.

a Investigate the number of letters in some 2-digit numbers.
Write your answers each time.

Like this:

The number **24** has ten letters. → 1 2 3 4 5 6 7 8 9 10 *twenty-four*

The number **31** has nine letters. → 1 2 3 4 5 6 7 8 9 *thirty-one*

b Which number has the **most** letters?

c Which has **least**?

d Which have the **same** number of letters?

1 'Less' strips

Recognising 1 less, 2 less and 3 less than a number (up to 20).

Copy and complete.

a 1 less

12	16	14	19	11	17	20	18	13	15
11									

b 2 less

13	16	19	14	20	17	12	11	15	18

c 3 less

11	16	18	14	12	17	19	13	20	15

2 Dice differences

Differences between two numbers (numbers up to 6).

Write the **difference** between the number of spots on each pair of dice.

Like this: difference is *2*.

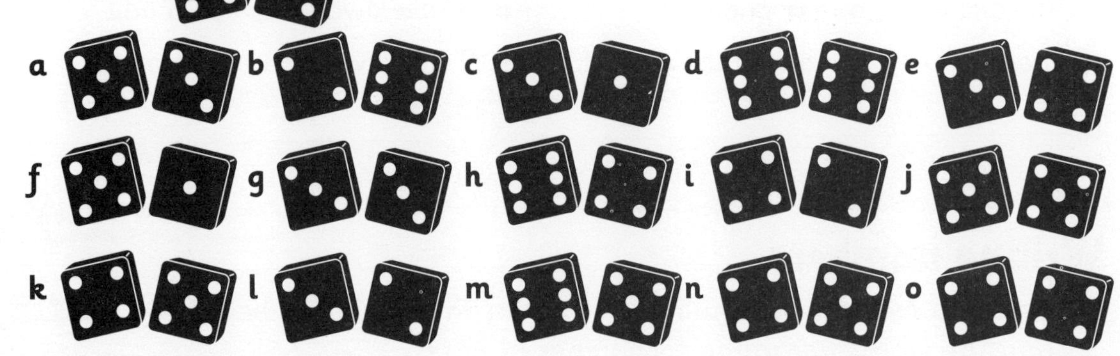

3 Subtraction grids

Subtracting one number from another (numbers up to 15).

Copy grid 2 each time.

Write numbers inside by subtracting from the numbers in grid 1.

Like this: 7 5 −2 = *3*

a grid 1

4	9	2
1	5	8
7	3	6

−1 =

grid 2

3		

b grid 1

3	9	5
7	6	2
10	4	8

−2 =

grid 2

4 Block graph

Interpreting a block graph.

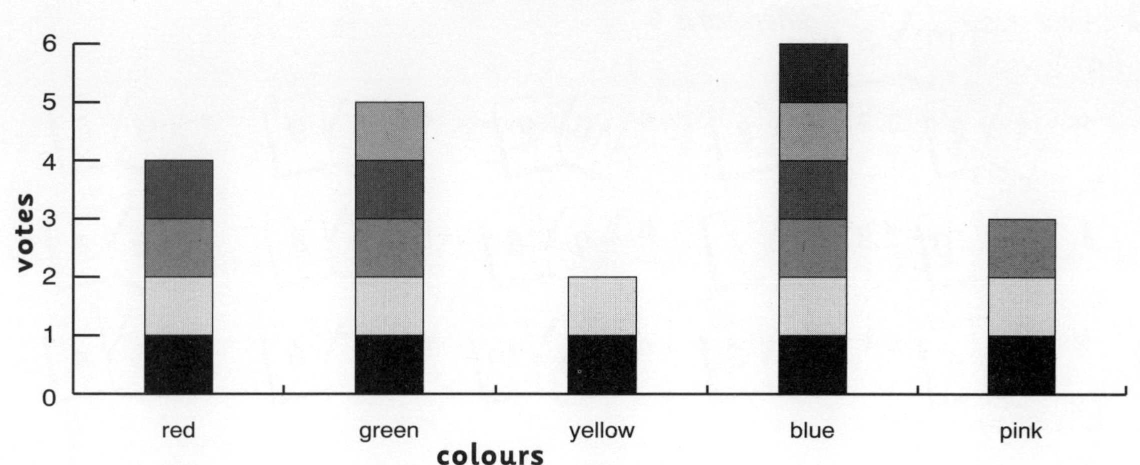

Use the block graph to help you answer the questions.

a Which colour is **most** popular?

b Which colour is **least** popular?

How many votes are there for:

c pink **d** green **e** red **f** blue **g** yellow

h How many **more** votes are there for blue than pink?

i How many **more** votes are there for green than yellow?

j How many **more** votes are there for red than pink?

k How many **fewer** votes are there for red than blue?

5 Pairs

Choosing pairs of numbers to make a given total.

Use cards numbered 1 to 16.

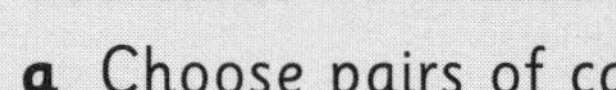

a Choose pairs of cards to total **16**. Write your additions each time.

Like this:  4 12 *4 + 12 = 16*  6 10 *6 + 10 = 16*

b How many **different** pairs can you make to total **15**. Write your additions.

c Choose other totals to investigate.

1 Card differences

Differences between two numbers (numbers up to 10).

Write the **difference** between the numbers on each pair of cards.

Like this: 7 3 *difference is 4*

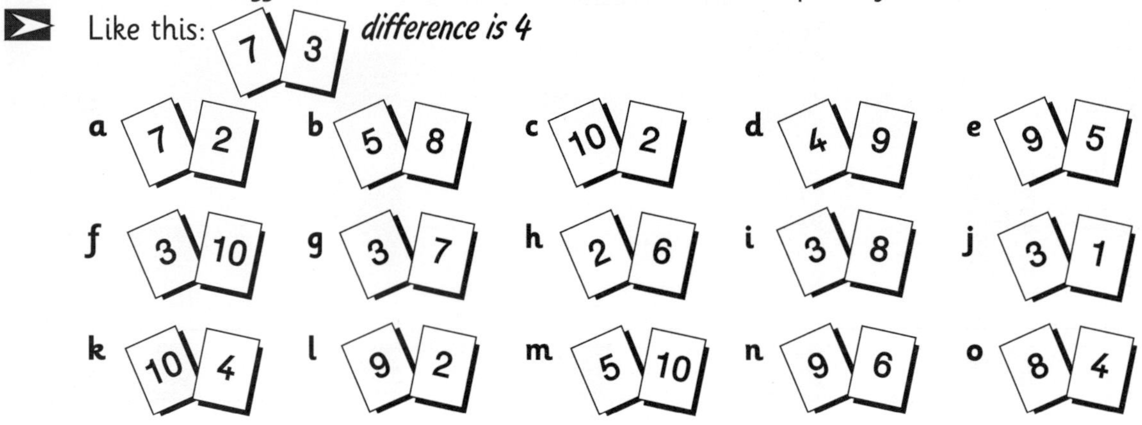

2 Number split

Expressing 2-digit numbers in extended form.

Split these numbers into tens and units.

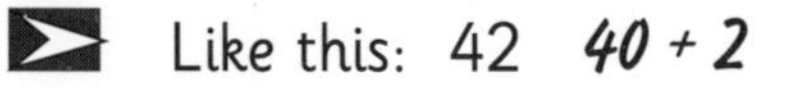

Like this: 42 *40 + 2*

a 32	**b** 17	**c** 89	**d** 53	**e** 25
f 76	**g** 48	**h** 37	**i** 62	**j** 94
k 59	**l** 90	**m** 27	**n** 41	**o** 68
p 36	**q** 14	**r** 85	**s** 73	**t** 44

3 Clocks

Reading a digital clock (quarter past, quarter to).

Write the time shown on these clocks.

Like this: 05:15 *quarter past 5*

a 03:15	**b** 09:45	**c** 06:15	**d** 06:45	**e** 01:15
f 03:45	**g** 08:45	**h** 02:15	**i** 02:30	**j** 01:45
k 10:15	**l** 08:00	**m** 11:45	**n** 04:15	**o** 05:45
p 10:45	**q** 11:15	**r** 12:45	**s** 07:30	**t** 09:15

4 Gaps

Writing 2-digit number names in numerals.

Write the missing numerals.

Like this: seventy-three 7__ *3*

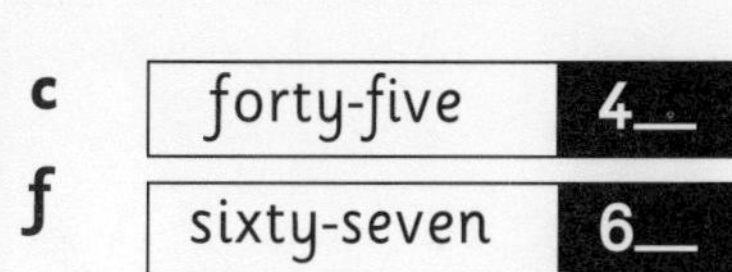

a thirty-four	3__	**b** twenty-one	__1	**c** forty-five	4__
d twenty-seven	__7	**e** ninety-two	__2	**f** sixty-seven	6__
g eighty-five	8__	**h** fifty-three	__3	**i** seventy-nine	__9
j thirty-six	3__	**k** seventy-three	7__	**l** forty-one	__1
m twenty-five	__5	**n** eighty-seven	8__	**o** forty-one	4__
p thirty-nine	__9	**q** sixty-two	__2	**r** ninety-seven	9__
s fifty-eight	__8	**t** seventy-five	7__	**u** fifty-nine	__9

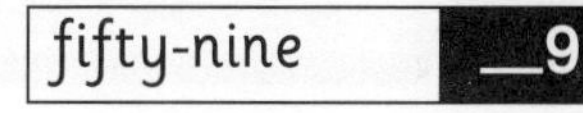

5 Adding coins

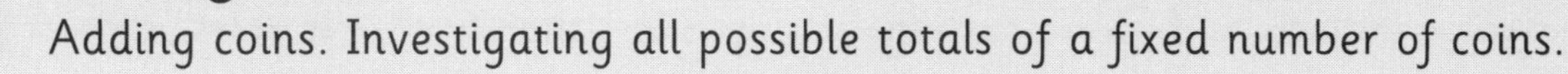

Adding coins. Investigating all possible totals of a fixed number of coins.

Use **two each** of these coins.  

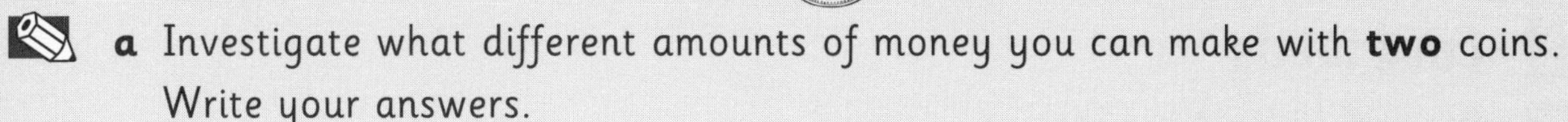

a Investigate what different amounts of money you can make with **two** coins.
Write your answers.

Like this:

1p + 1p = *2p*

5p + 1p = *6p*

b What amounts can you make with **three** coins each time?

1 Darts

Adding two numbers (totals up to 20).

Write the total score for these pairs of darts of the same colour.

Like this: **a** *8 + 7 = 15*

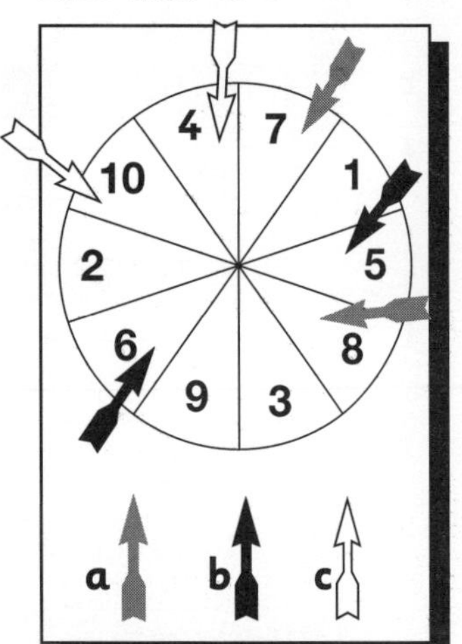

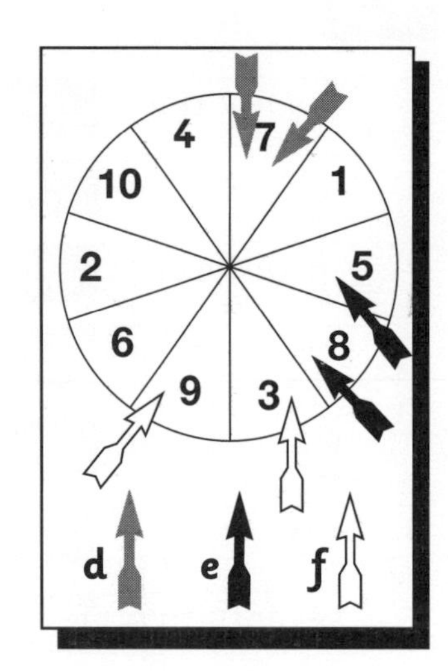

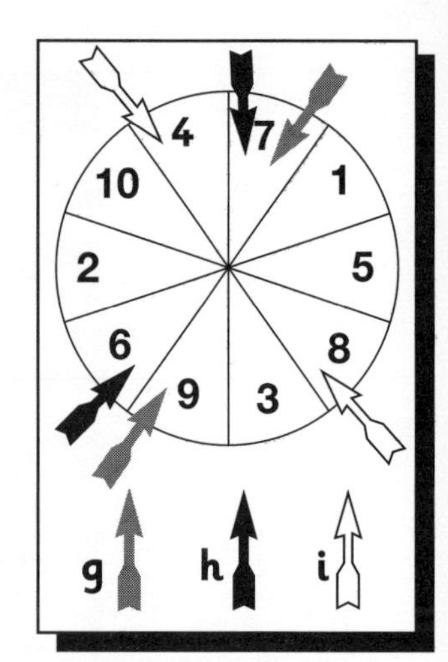

2 More or less

Recognising numbers which are more or less than a given number.

Write numbers to match the questions.

Like this: 3 more than 5 *8*

a 2 more than 4	**b** 2 less than 5	**c** 3 more than 5	**d** 1 less than 7
e 4 more than 6	**f** 5 more than 1	**g** 3 less than 8	**h** 4 less than 6
i 2 more than 3	**j** 2 less than 10	**k** 4 more than 4	**l** 1 less than 8
m 3 less than 4	**n** 5 more than 4	**o** 2 less than 3	**p** 5 less than 7

3 Card totals

Addition facts up to 20.

Write the **total** of the numbers on each pair of cards.

Like this: 7 12 total is *19*

a 12 2

b 6 13

c 

d 

e 

f 5 14

g 11 3

h 13 5

i 

j 

k 7 13

l 12 3

m 4 12

n 15 5

o 13 3

4 Choosing numbers

Vertical subtraction (numbers up to 10).

Choose two of the numbers to make the subtractions work. Write your subtractions.

Like this: 2 5 7

□ − □ = 3 → 5 − 2 = 3

	Numbers	Answer
a	3 5 9	6
b	1 3 7	6
c	3 4 8	5
d	2 5 9	4
e	1 2 6	4
f	1 3 5	2
g	2 6 8	6
h	2 3 4	2
i	4 5 6	2
j	3 5 7	4

5 Block graph

Collecting data, drawing and interpreting a block graph.

You need a dice.

a Throw the dice **20 times** and write the scores.

b Draw a block graph on squared paper to show your results.

c Write about your block graph.

Like this:

1 Jumping addition

Addition facts up to 20.

Write the answers to these additions. Use the number line to help you.

Like this: 8 add 5 *13*

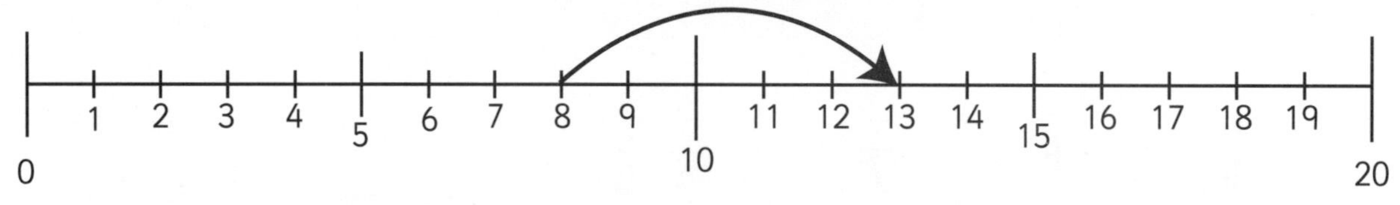

a 5 add 7	**b** 11 add 4	**c** 13 add 2	**d** 6 add 8	**e** 5 add 9
f 9 add 3	**g** 12 add 4	**h** 3 add 11	**i** 10 add 4	**j** 13 add 5
k 12 add 6	**l** 14 add 1	**m** 7 add 5	**n** 4 add 13	**o** 16 add 2

2 Strips of pairs

Finding pairs of numbers to make 20.

Copy the strips. Write numbers in the bottom row.

a make 20

14	8	19	5	16	3	12	9	2	13
6									

b make 20

5	13	1	18	11	4	17	9	15	7

3 Number lines

Finding points on a number line marked in ones.

Write the position of each letter on the lines.

Like this: **a** *43*

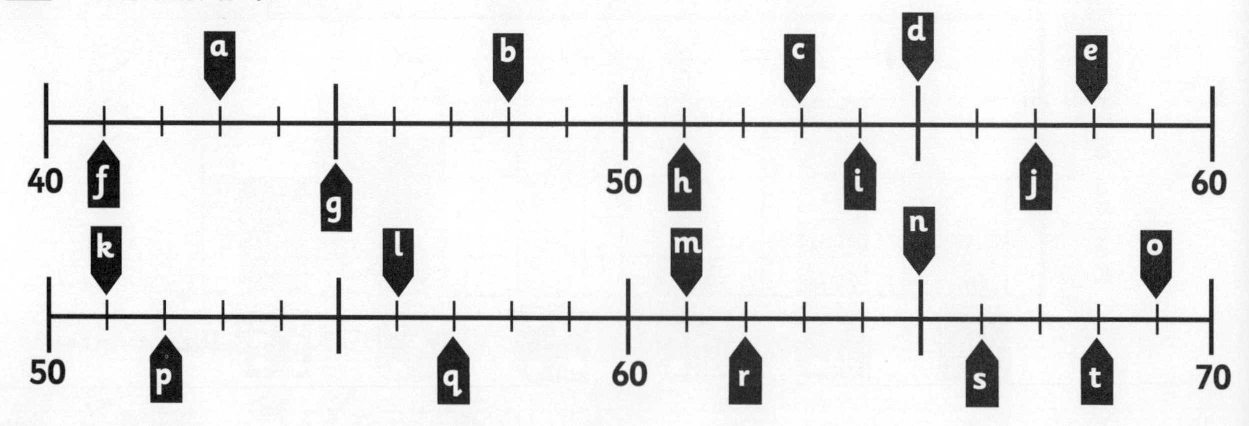

4 Swap two

Ordering a set of 2-digit numbers.

Swap two numbers to put each list in order.

Like this: 35 36 39 38 37 40 swap *37 and 39*

a 21 24 23 22 25 26

b 53 54 57 56 55 58

c 70 74 72 73 71 75

d 15 21 18 19 20 16

e 25 24 23 26 27 28

f 35 40 37 38 39 36

g 90 89 88 91 92 93

h 46 52 49 50 47 53

i 29 31 38 37 41 42

j 15 27 45 36 53 62

k 18 56 47 35 64 75

l 34 39 52 71 63 82

5 Amounts of coins

Adding coins. Investigating all possible totals of a fixed number of coins.

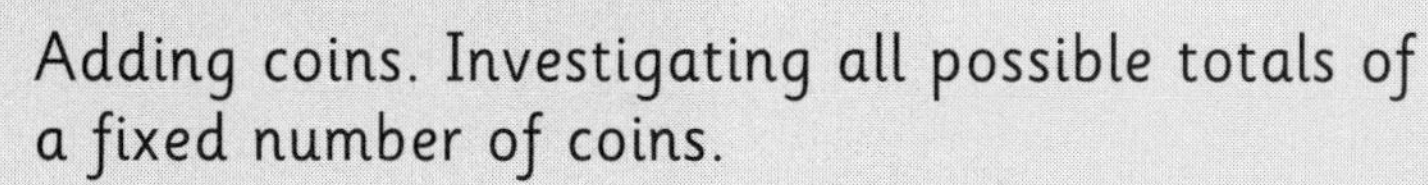

Use **two each** of these coins. 

a Investigate what different amounts of money you can make with **two** coins.
Write your answers.

Like this:

2p + 2p = *4p*

1p + 10p = *11p*

b What amounts can you make with **three** coins each time?

1 Adding

Horizontal addition (totals up to 20).

Copy and complete these additions.

Like this: *13 + 2 = 15*

a 3 + 12	**b** 11 + 5	**c** 7 + 7	**d** 13 + 4
e 16 + 2	**f** 8 + 9	**g** 4 + 12	**h** 14 + 3
i 13 + 6	**j** 6 + 9	**k** 10 + 7	**l** 18 + 2
m 3 + 14	**n** 5 + 11	**o** 12 + 7	**p** 5 + 8
q 9 + 7	**r** 14 + 5	**s** 17 + 2	**t** 15 + 3

2 What's the number?

Recognising the value of numbers written in extended form.

Write the value of these numbers.

Like this: 50 + 6 *56*

a 40 + 4	**b** 60 + 7	**c** 30 + 1	**d** 80 + 9	**e** 10 + 3
f 70 + 6	**g** 5 + 20	**h** 4 + 90	**i** 50 + 2	**j** 60 + 8
k 30 + 4	**l** 9 + 10	**m** 70 + 3	**n** 5 + 90	**o** 1 + 20
p 80 + 6	**q** 60 + 7	**r** 2 + 50	**s** 30 + 8	**t** 3 + 40

3 Clocks

Reading an analogue clock (5-minute times).

Write the time shown on these clocks.

Like this:  *20 past 3*

a  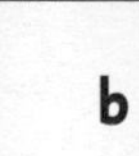
b 
c 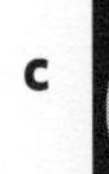 
d  
e 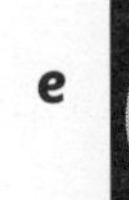

f 
g 
h 
i 
j 

k 
l 
m
n 
o 

4 Adding machines

Adding on (totals up to 20).

Like this: **+3**

in	7
out	*10*

Copy and complete the tables for these machines.

a +3

in	8	12	15	4	10	16	7	14	9	13
out										

b +7

in	8	3	11	6	12	10	5	7	13	9
out										

c +12

in	3	5	8	0	6	2	7	4	10	1
out										

5 Making numbers

Ordering a set of 2-digit numbers; creating 2-digit numbers from that set.

a Choose three numerals.

Like this: **4, 3, 6**

b Use them to make **six** different 2-digit numbers.

46, 43, 64, 63, 34, 36

You can use use each numeral only **once**.

c Now write them in order from **smallest** to **largest**.

d Keep trying with different sets of 3 numerals each time.

1 Writing numerals

Writing 2-digit number names.

Write the number shown by the beads on each abacus.

Like this: *thirty-five*

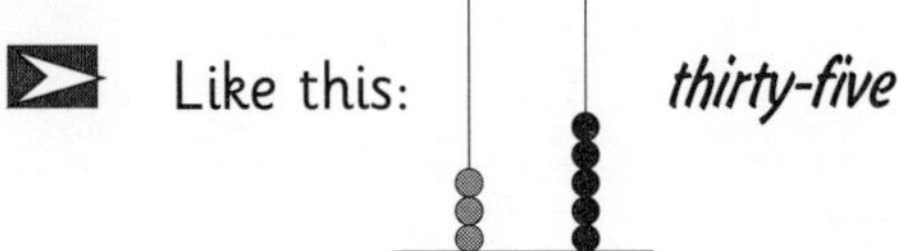

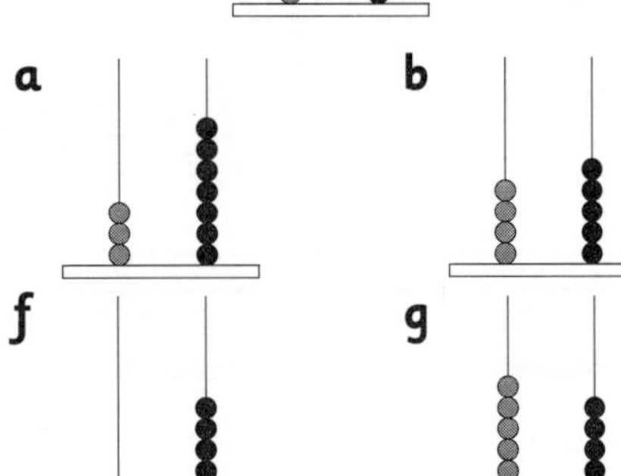

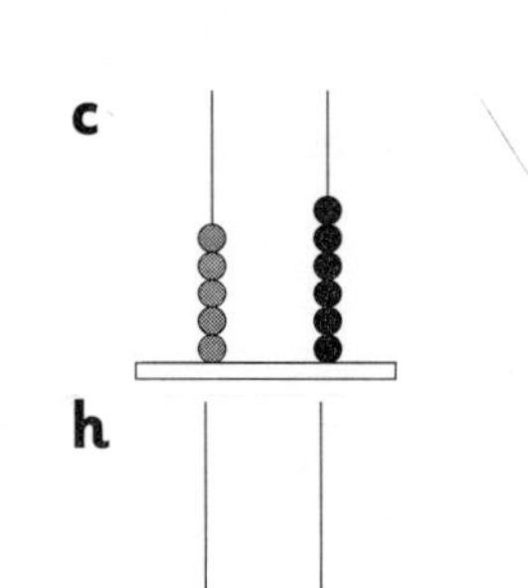

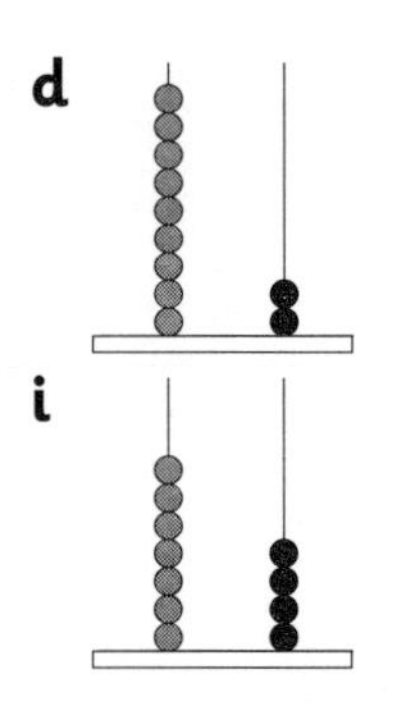

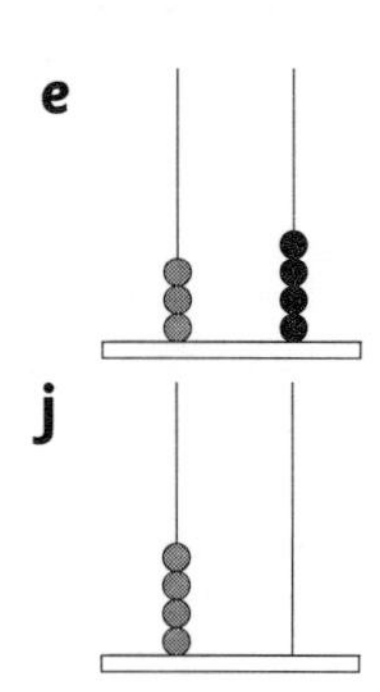

2 Subtracting

Vertical subtraction (numbers up to 20).

Copy and complete these subtractions.

Like this:

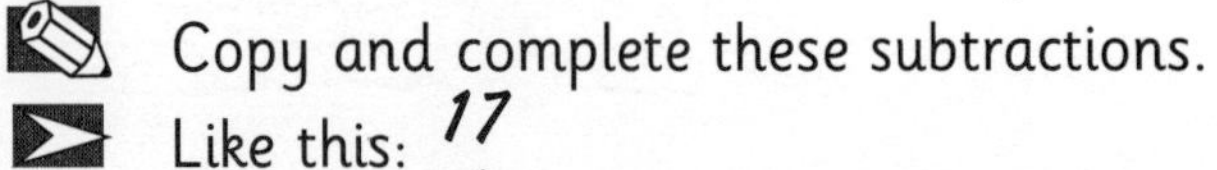

$$\begin{array}{r} 17 \\ -\ 4 \\ \hline 13 \end{array}$$

a $\begin{array}{r} 17 \\ -\ 6 \\ \hline \end{array}$	**b** $\begin{array}{r} 12 \\ -\ 7 \\ \hline \end{array}$	**c** $\begin{array}{r} 18 \\ -\ 5 \\ \hline \end{array}$	**d** $\begin{array}{r} 16 \\ -\ 2 \\ \hline \end{array}$	**e** $\begin{array}{r} 13 \\ -\ 3 \\ \hline \end{array}$	**f** $\begin{array}{r} 11 \\ -\ 8 \\ \hline \end{array}$	**g** $\begin{array}{r} 19 \\ -\ 6 \\ \hline \end{array}$	**h** $\begin{array}{r} 14 \\ -\ 7 \\ \hline \end{array}$
i $\begin{array}{r} 15 \\ -\ 3 \\ \hline \end{array}$	**j** $\begin{array}{r} 20 \\ -\ 7 \\ \hline \end{array}$	**k** $\begin{array}{r} 19 \\ -\ 11 \\ \hline \end{array}$	**l** $\begin{array}{r} 16 \\ -\ 5 \\ \hline \end{array}$	**m** $\begin{array}{r} 20 \\ -\ 5 \\ \hline \end{array}$	**n** $\begin{array}{r} 17 \\ -\ 8 \\ \hline \end{array}$	**o** $\begin{array}{r} 13 \\ -\ 4 \\ \hline \end{array}$	**p** $\begin{array}{r} 15 \\ -\ 1 \\ \hline \end{array}$

3 Card differences

Differences between two numbers (numbers up to 10).

Write the **difference** between the numbers on each pair of cards.

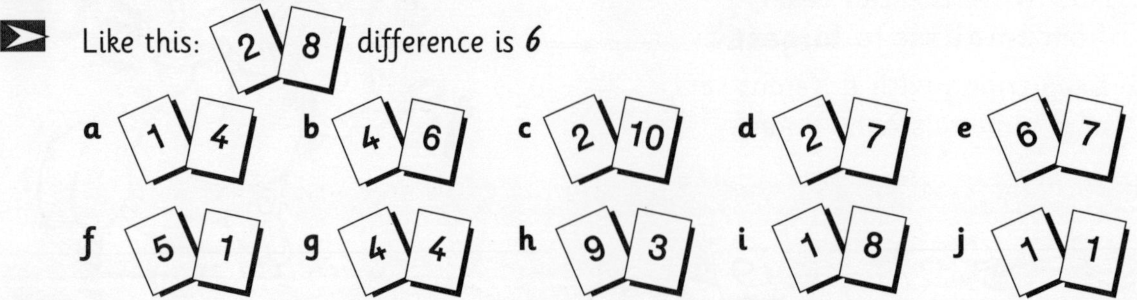

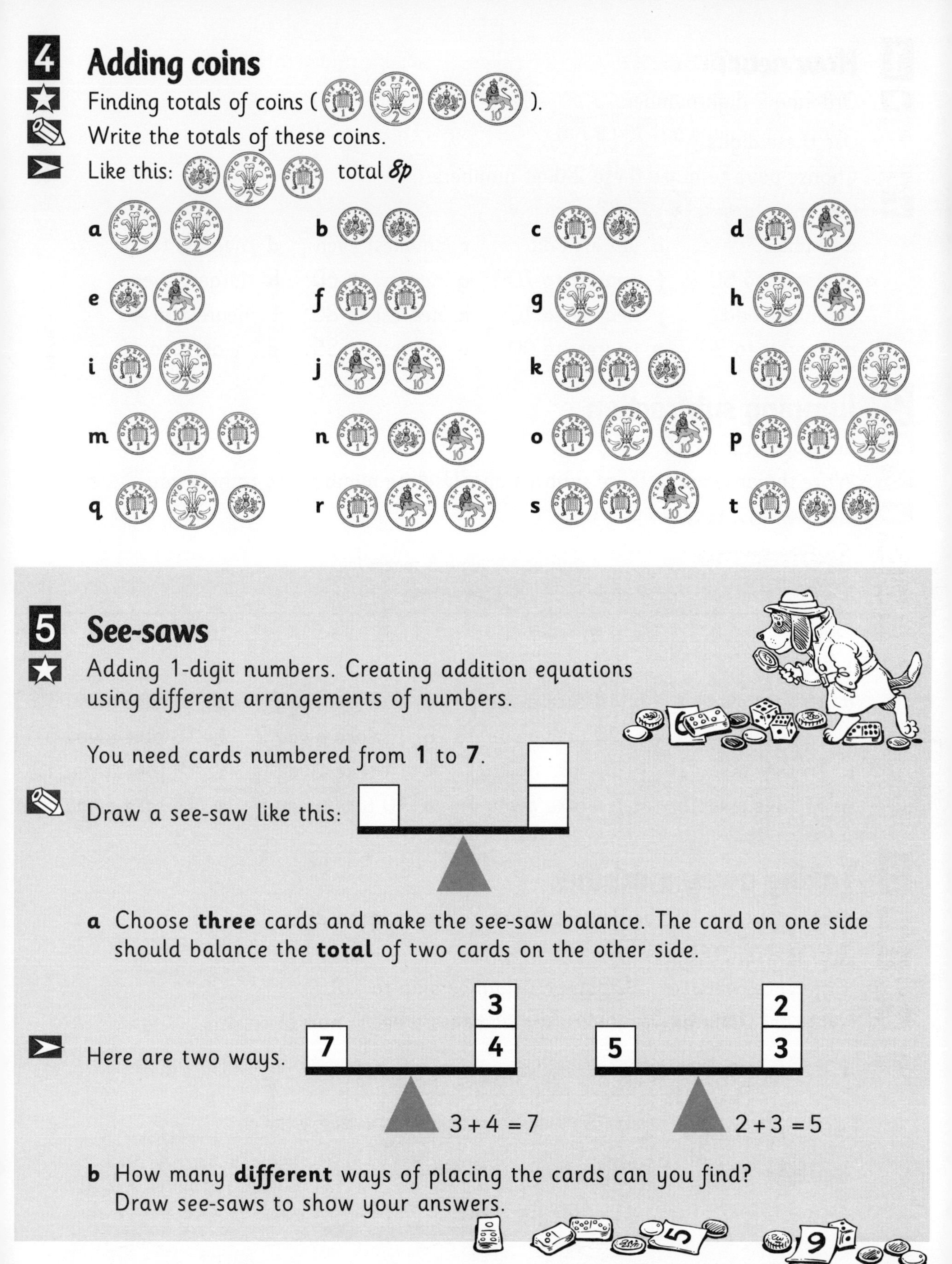

4 Adding coins

Finding totals of coins ( ).

Write the totals of these coins.

Like this: total *8p*

a b c d

e f g h

i j k l

m n o p

q r s t

5 See-saws

Adding 1-digit numbers. Creating addition equations using different arrangements of numbers.

You need cards numbered from **1** to **7**.

Draw a see-saw like this:

a Choose **three** cards and make the see-saw balance. The card on one side should balance the **total** of two cards on the other side.

Here are two ways.

b How many **different** ways of placing the cards can you find? Draw see-saws to show your answers.

1 How near?

★ Ordering 2-digit numbers.

Use these digits. 5 7 2 8

Choose pairs to make these 2-digit numbers.

➤ Like this: largest 8 7 *87*

a smallest	**b** largest odd	**c** smallest even	**d** nearest to 20
e nearest to 50	**f** nearest to 70	**g** nearest to 60	**h** largest even
i smallest odd	**j** nearest to 10	**k** nearest to 80	**l** nearest to 40
m nearest to 30	**n** nearest to 90	**o** nearest to 35	**p** nearest to 45

2 Jumping subtraction

★ Subtraction from 20.

✎ Write the answers to these subtractions. Use the number line to help you.

➤ Like this: 12 take away 3 is *9*

start at 12, jump 3 spaces left

0 1 2 3 4 5 6 7 8 9 10 11 12 13 14 15 16 17 18 19 20

a 15 take away 3	**b** 18 take away 4	**c** 7 take away 3	**d** 16 take away 15
e 13 take away 4	**f** 20 take away 13	**g** 11 take away 2	**h** 18 take away 5
i 16 take away 14	**j** 20 take away 11	**k** 14 take away 9	**l** 19 take away 10
m 11 take away 5	**n** 17 take away 7	**o** 10 take away 6	**p** 15 take away 6

3 Taking away machines

★ Subtracting one number from another (numbers up to 20).

➤ Like this: take away 3

in	8
out	*5*

✎ Copy and complete the tables for these machines.

a

in	17	9	13	10	20	5	7	18	6	11
out										

b

in	9	13	11	18	7	10	16	12	8	14
out										

4 Targets

Adding two numbers (totals up to 20).

Write the total score for these pairs of shots at the target.

Like this: **a** *8 + 8 = 16*

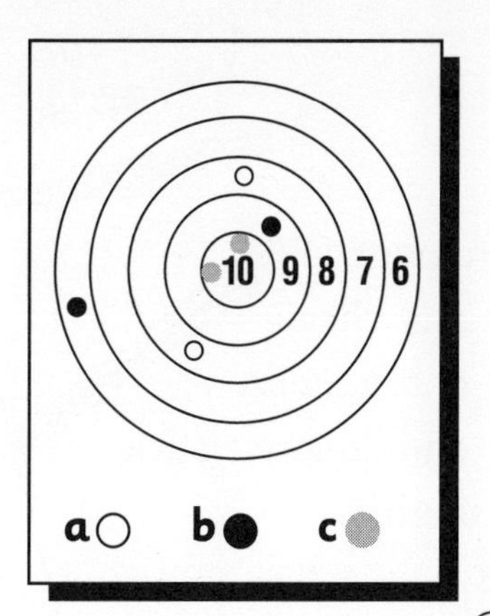

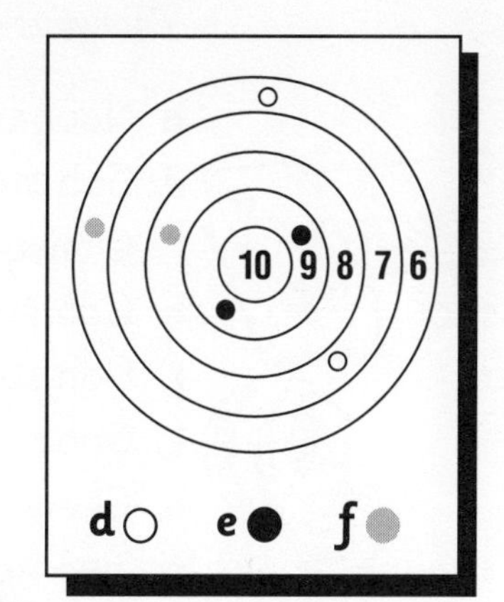

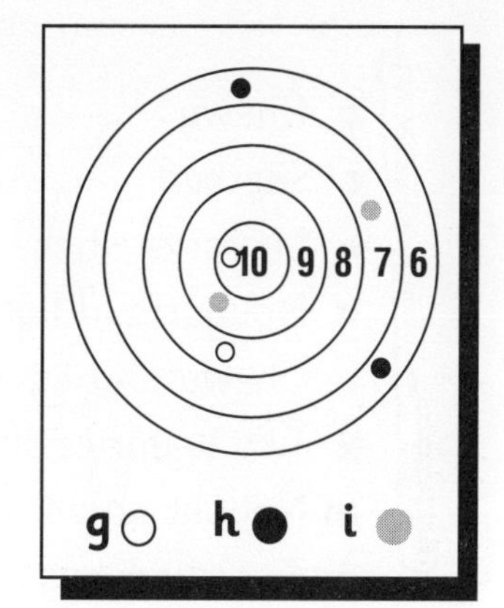

Domino pairs

Adding spots on pairs of dominoes; sorting them according to totals.

You need a set of dominoes.

a Find a pair of dominoes with a total of 10 spots. Show your answers.

Like this:

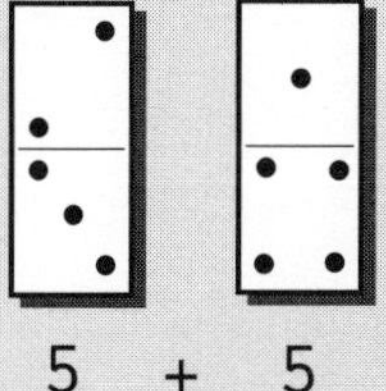

5 + 5 = 10

b How many **other pairs** can you make with a **total** of **10** spots? Show your answers.

c Investigate a total of **8** spots.

d Investigate **other** totals of spots.

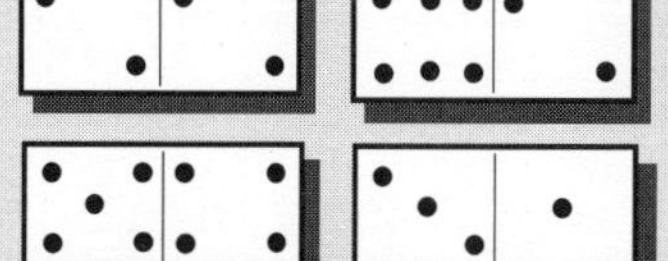

1 Change

Finding change from 10p.

How much change would you get from 10p for these?

Like this: Gob stopper and nougat *Cost 1p and 5p, total 6p*
Change is 4p

Price List
Chewy 2p
Gob stopper 1p
Nougat 5p
Liquorice stick 3p
Sherbert 4p

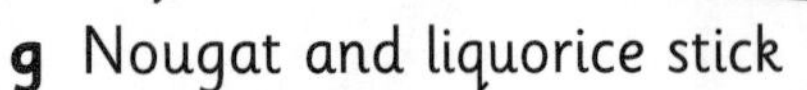

a Chewy
b Nougat
c Sherbert
d Gob stopper
e Liquorice stick
f Chewy and nougat
g Nougat and liquorice stick
h Gob stopper and chewy
i Chewy and liquorice stick
j Gob stopper and nougat
k Two liquorice sticks
l Gob stopper and liquorice stick
m Nougat and sherbert
n Chewy and sherbert
o Two sherberts
p Two nougats
q Gob stopper and sherbert
r Liquorice stick and sherbert
s Two chewies
t Two gob stoppers

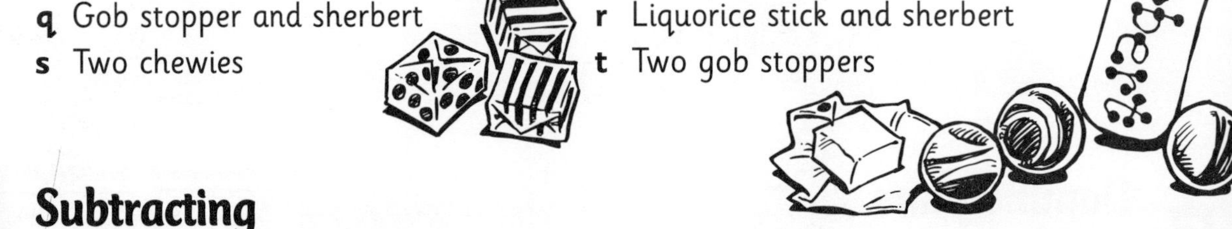

2 Subtracting

Horizontal subtraction (numbers up to 20).

Copy and complete these subtractions.

Like this: *14 - 6 = 8*

a 15 – 2	**b** 19 – 2	**c** 17 – 6	**d** 16 – 3	**e** 18 – 1
f 13 – 5	**g** 11 – 4	**h** 20 – 3	**i** 12 – 7	**j** 16 – 6
k 19 – 7	**l** 17 –2	**m** 18 – 4	**n** 15 – 9	**o** 20 – 5
p 18 –15	**q** 16 – 11	**r** 17 – 14	**s** 20 – 13	**t** 19 – 13

3 More or less

Recognising numbers which are more or less than a given number.

Write numbers to match the questions.

Like this: 3 less than 9 *6*

a 1 more than 5	**b** 4 less than 12	**c** 9 less than 16	**d** 3 more than 16
e 6 less than 13	**f** 9 more than 8	**g** 8 less than 17	**h** 5 more than 6
i 6 less than 15	**j** 4 less than 19	**k** 2 more than 12	**l** 9 less than 14
m 4 more than 13	**n** 10 less than 18	**o** 8 more than 7	**p** 11 less than 20

4 Block graph

★ Drawing a block graph.

These are the scores when a dice is thrown 20 times.

2	5	3	1	4	2	6	4	6	4
4	2	1	4	3	6	2	1	6	4

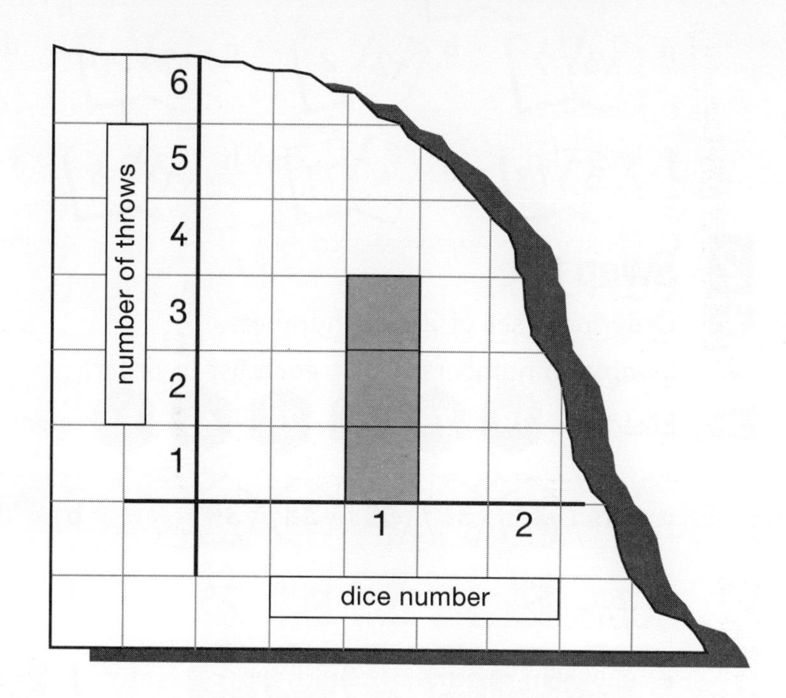

a Copy and complete this block graph to show the scores.
Use squared paper.

5 Arrows

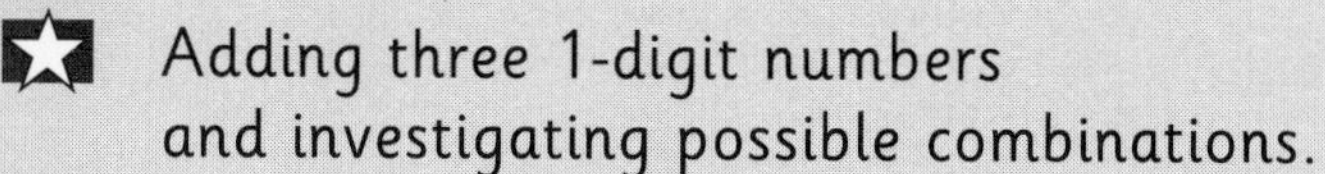

★ Adding three 1-digit numbers and investigating possible combinations.

You have three arrows to aim at this target.

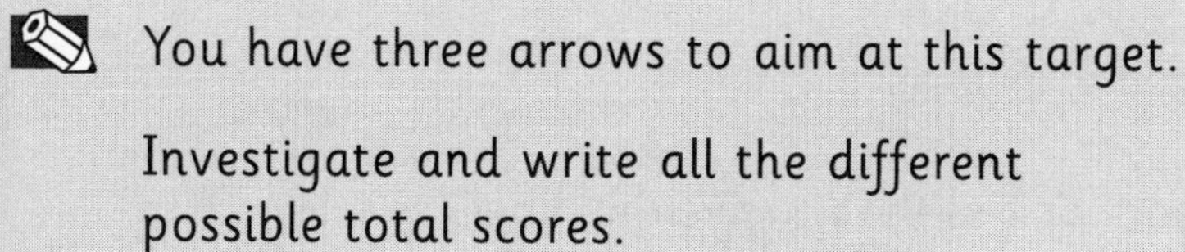

Investigate and write all the different possible total scores.

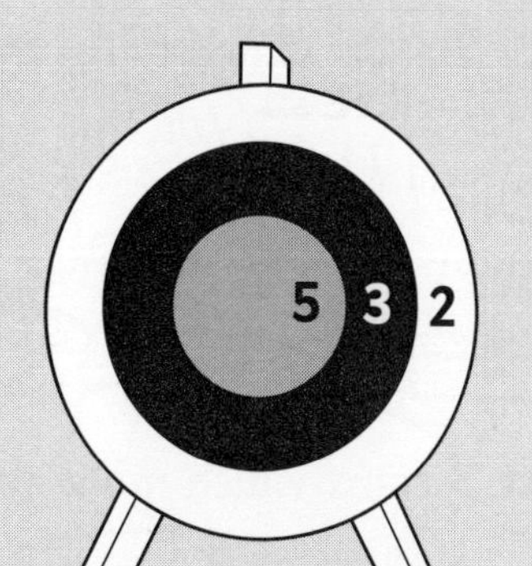

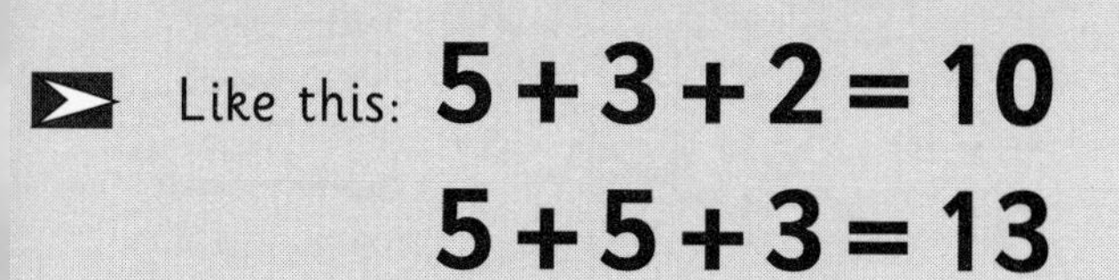

Like this: **5 + 3 + 2 = 10**

5 + 5 + 3 = 13

1 Card differences

Differences between two numbers (numbers up to 20).

Write the **difference** between the numbers on each pair of cards.

Like this: 13 5 difference is *8*

a 13 7   b 12 4   c 12 20   d 3 11   e 3 16

f 5 13   g 4 11   h 11 5   i 7 11   j 4 13

2 Swap two

Ordering a set of 2-digit numbers.

Swap two numbers to put each list in order.

Like this: 19 26 38 27 45 51 swap *27 and 38*

a 34 37 36 35 38 39

b 91 92 95 94 97 98

c 53 57 56 54 58 59

d 40 42 46 44 47 48

e 91 84 86 89 90 83

f 25 27 32 31 29 33

g 48 52 50 51 49 60

h 71 75 78 95 92 83

3 Prices

Choosing coins to make an exact amount.

Use these coins.

Write **2** coins which make these prices exactly.

Like this: 11p *10p, 1p*

a 3p   b 12p   c 2p   d 7p   e 6p

Write **3** coins which make these prices exactly.

f 5p   g 3p   h 11p   i 7p   j 13p

4 Subtraction grids

Subtracting one number from another (numbers up to 20).

Copy grid 2 each time.

Write numbers inside by subtracting from the numbers in grid 1.

Like this: 8 5 / 1 −3 = 2

a grid 1 −3 = grid 2

12	8	5
6	13	11
10	9	7

9		

b grid 1 −5 = grid 2

17	13	7
11	6	15
8	16	9

12		

c grid 1 −4 = grid 2

7	20	9
8	12	15
11	16	5

		1

d grid 1 −2 = grid 2

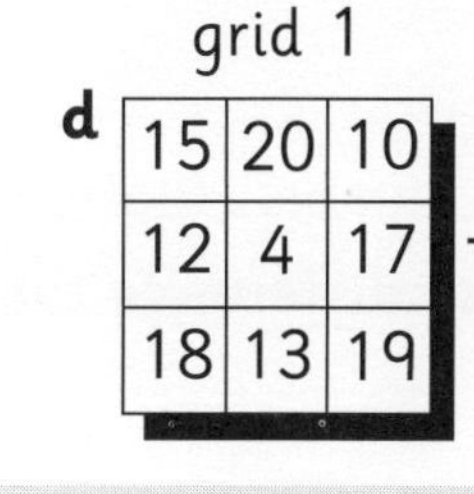

15	20	10
12	4	17
18	13	19

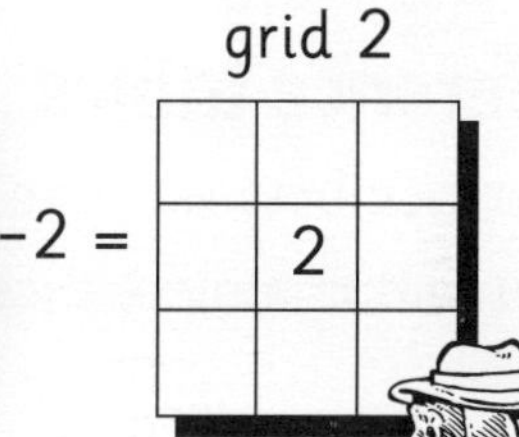

	2	

5 Names

Counting the number of letters in first names.
Collecting, sorting and interpreting data.

a Count the number of letters in each of these popular names. Write your answers.

b Count the number of letters in other names. (Think of your friends or family.)

c Which number of letters is the most common?

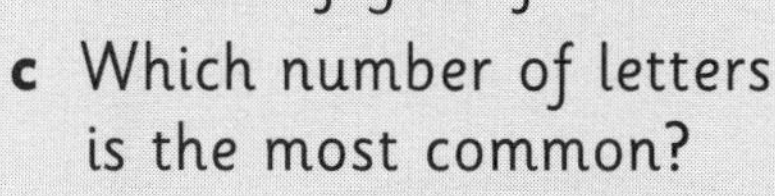

Popular names

The ten most popular boy's names in 1990 were: James, Thomas, William, Alexander, Edward, Charles, Oliver, Nicholas, Christopher, Henry.

1 How near?

Ordering 2-digit numbers.

Use these digits. 1 4 5 9

Choose pairs to make these 2-digit numbers.

Like this: largest 9 5 *95*

a smallest
b largest odd
c smallest even
d nearest to 20
e nearest to 50
f nearest to 70
g nearest to 60
h largest even
i smallest odd
j nearest to 10
k nearest to 80
l nearest to 40
m nearest to 30
n nearest to 90
o nearest to 35
p nearest to 45
q nearest to 55
r nearest to 65

2 Difference tables

Difference between two numbers (up to 20).

Copy and complete these **difference** tables.

a

	1	12	19
4	*3*		
11			
17			

b

	15	6	3
2			
5			
8			

c

	13	18	7
20			
10			
14			

3 'More' strips

Recognising 10 more and 20 more than a number (up to 100).

Copy and complete.

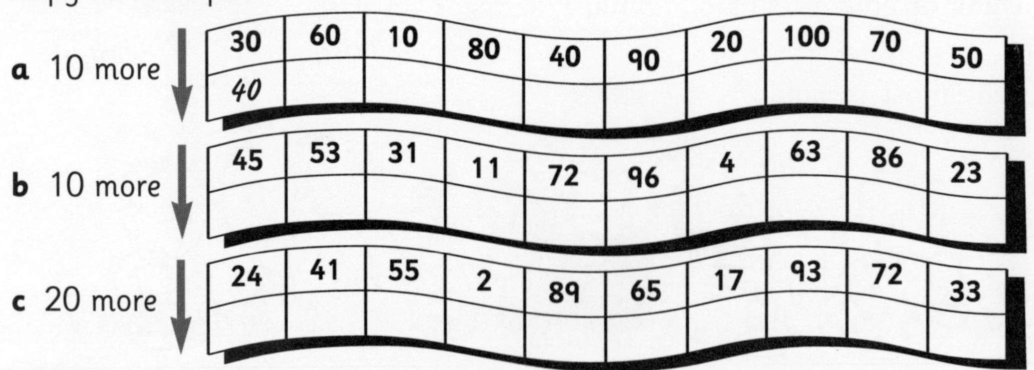

4 Targets

Adding two numbers (totals up to 20).

Write the total score for these pairs of shots at the target.

Like this: **a** $2 + 2 = 4$

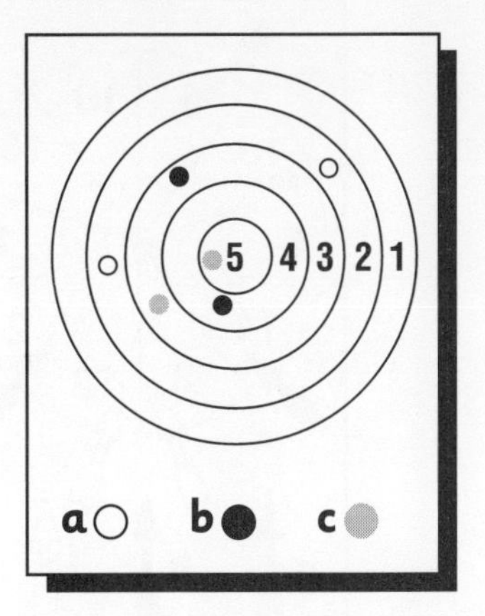

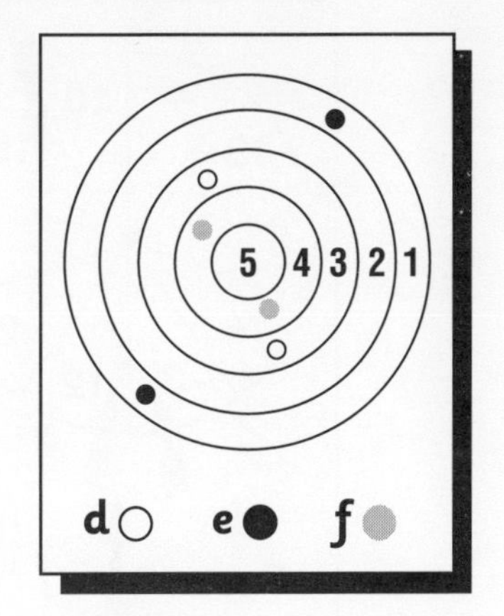

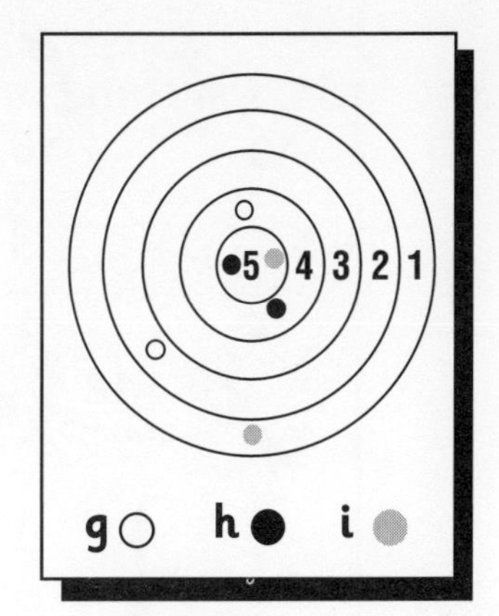

5 3 Dice

Recognising odd and even spots on dice.
Investigating different arrangements of dice.

You need three dice. 

a Arrange the dice so that they **all** show an **odd** number of spots.
Draw your dice numbers.

Like this:   

Rule  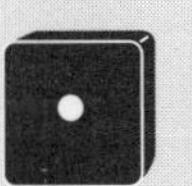  is the same as   

b Investigate different ways of doing this. Draw your dice numbers each time.

c How many ways can you find?

1 Darts

Adding two numbers (totals up to 20).

Write the total score for these pairs of darts.

Like this: **a** *2 + 11 = 13*

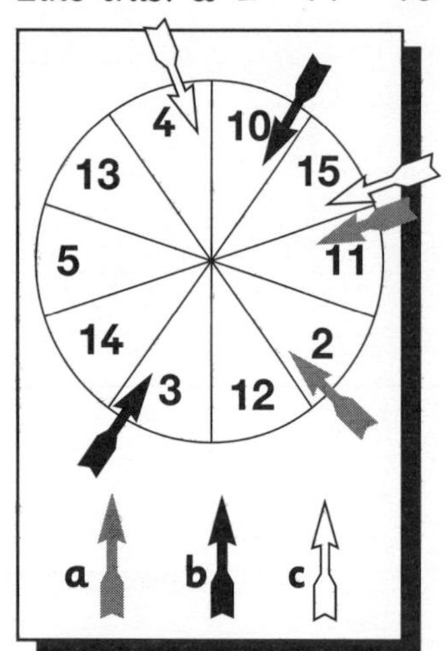

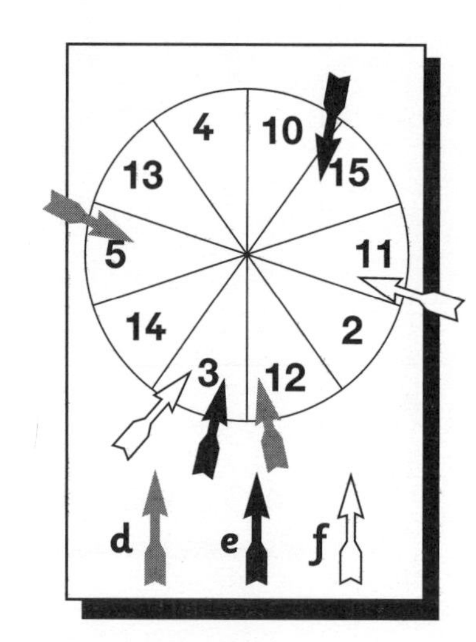

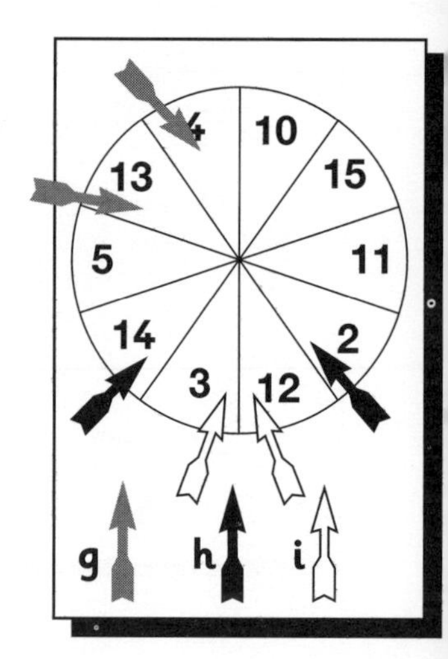

2 Jumping forwards and backwards

Addition and subtraction facts to 20.

Write the answers to these additions and subtractions. Use the number line to help yo

Like this: 14 take away 3 *11* 14 add 3 *17*

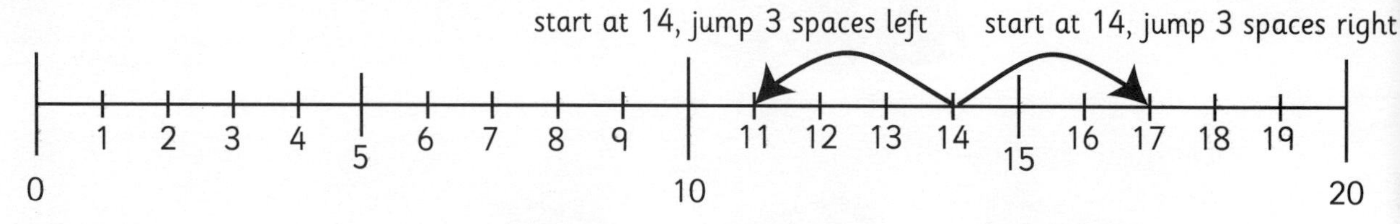

a 5 add 4	**b** 13 take away 3	**c** 6 add 9	**d** 7 add 6
e 15 take away 3	**f** 19 take away 2	**g** 11 add 4	**h** 9 take away 3
i 12 take away 4	**j** 17 take away 5	**k** 14 add 5	**l** 8 add 3

3 Fractions

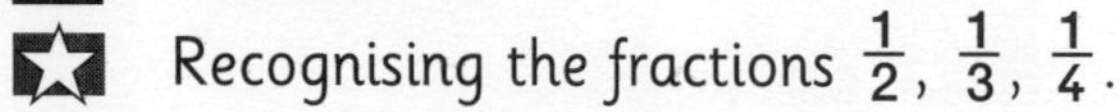

Recognising the fractions $\frac{1}{2}$, $\frac{1}{3}$, $\frac{1}{4}$.

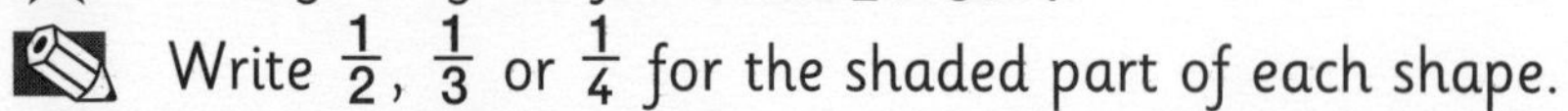

Write $\frac{1}{2}$, $\frac{1}{3}$ or $\frac{1}{4}$ for the shaded part of each shape.

Like this: $\frac{1}{3}$

a 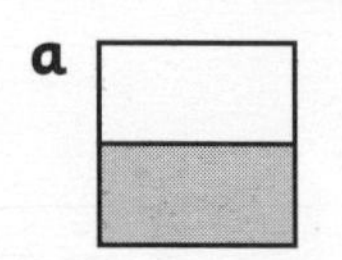

b 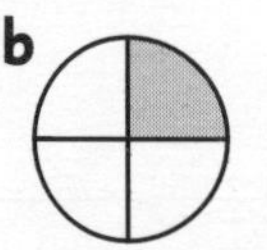

c 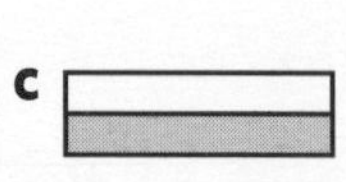

d 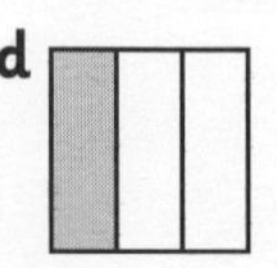

e 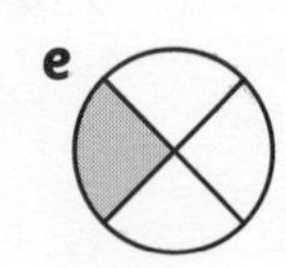

f 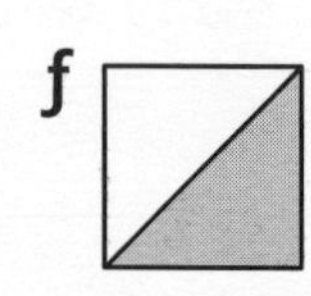

g 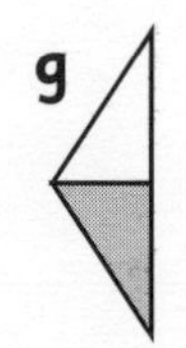

4 Stamps

Adding two sums of money (totals up to 50p).

Here are 5 different stamps.

Write the total cost of sending a letter with these pairs of stamps.

a  and

b  and

c  and

d and

e  and

f and

g and

h and

i  and

j  and 

k  and

l  and

m  and

n  and 

o  and 

p  and 

5 Difference pairs

Choosing pairs of numbers with the same difference.

Use cards numbered from 1 to 16.

a Choose pairs of cards with a difference of **9**.
Write the difference each time.

Like this: **10** – **1** = *9*   **14** – **5** = *9*

b How many **different** pairs can you find with a difference of 9?

c Investigate pairs with a difference of **6**.

d Choose other differences to investigate.

1 Clocks

Reading a digital clock (5 minute times).

Write the time shown on these clocks:

Like this: 01:20 *twenty past 1*

a 05:10	**b** 01:40	**c** 03:20	**d** 07:00	**e** 06:50
f 08:05	**g** 02:30	**h** 11:25	**i** 02:35	**j** 01:50
k 09:15	**l** 06:30	**m** 08:40	**n** 03:45	**o** 04:05
p 05:55	**q** 10:25	**r** 04:20	**s** 07:15	**t** 12:10

2 'Less' strips

Recognising 10 less and 20 less than a number (up to 100).

Copy and complete.

a 10 less

30	50	10	80	60	90	20	100	40	70
20									

b 10 less

13	61	46	94	24	76	107	35	83	57

c 20 less

34	77	59	86	25	68	94	43	105	117

3 Addition tables

Addition facts (totals up to 10).

Copy and complete these **addition** tables.

a

+	1	3	0
4	*5*		
2			
5			

b

+	4	2	5
1			
3			
5			

c

+	3	1	0
0			
4			
2			

4 Card differences

Differences between 2 numbers (numbers up to 20).

Write the **difference** between the numbers on each pair of cards.

Like this: *difference is 9*

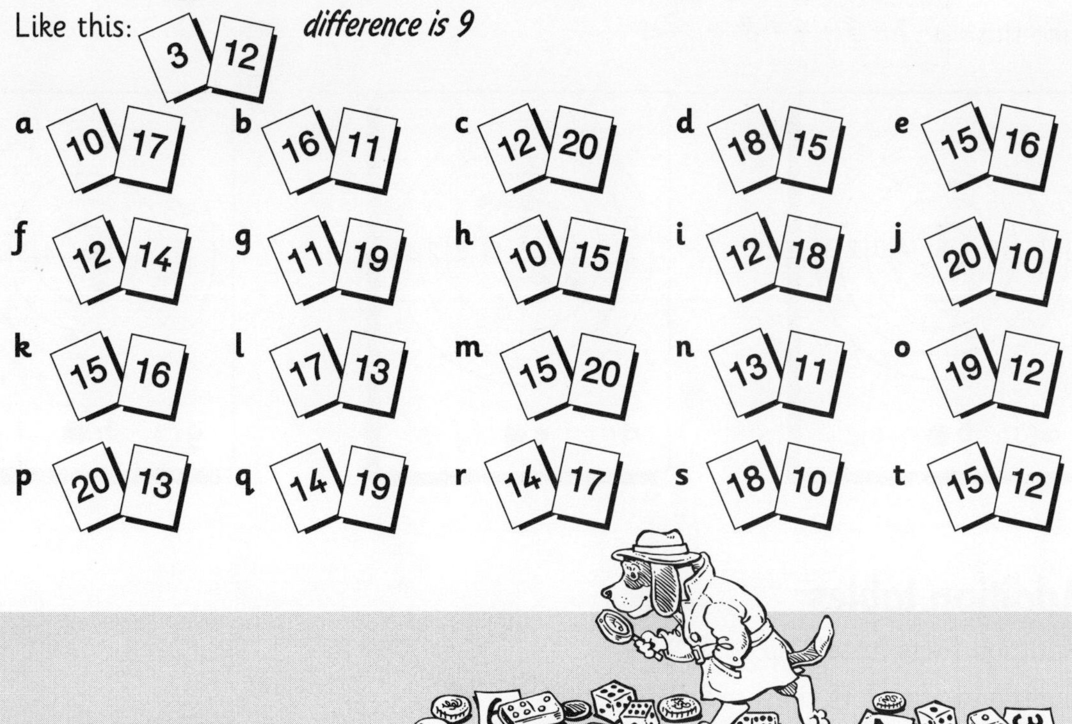

5 Different subtractions

Subtracting one 1-digit number from another.
Investigating different possible subtractions when choosing two numbers.

You need six cards numbered like this.

Make a subtraction by choosing **two** of the cards.
What is the result?

Like this: 5 – 4 = *1*

a Investigate **all** the different possible results when choosing two cards.
Write your subtraction and result each time.

1 Targets

★ Adding 3 numbers (totals up to 15).

✎ Write the total score for these pairs of shots at the target.

➤ Like this: **a** *1 + 3 + 4 = 8*

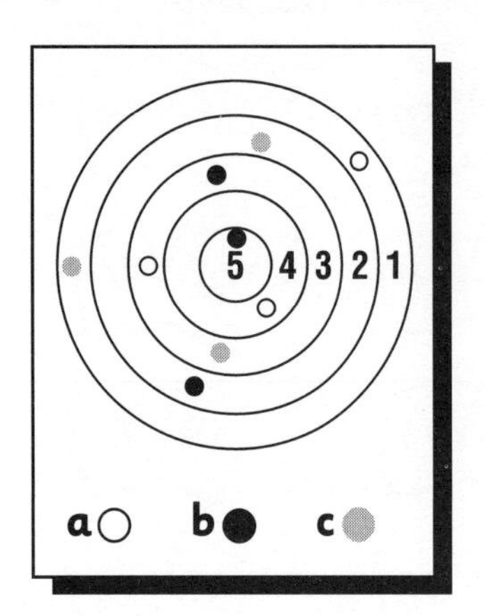

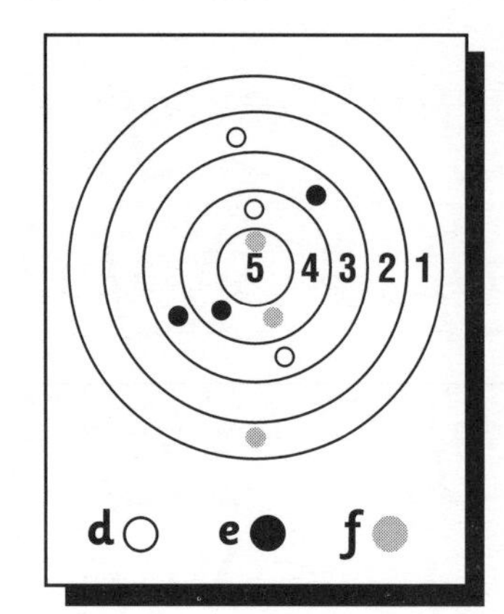

2 Addition tables

★ Addition facts (totals up to 20).

✎ Copy and complete these **addition** tables.

a

+	3	5	7
12	*15*		
9			
6			

b

+	8	6	11
4			
11			
5			

c

+	9	13	10
3			
7			
4			

3 Change

★ Finding change from 20p.

✎ How much change would you get from 20p for each of these?

➤ Like this: Flapjack 4p *16p*

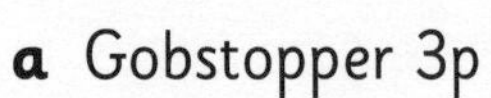

a Gobstopper 3p

b Chew 1p

c Mintoes 5p

d Fruit pastels 8p

e Bubble gum 2p

f Lolly 7p

g Chewing gum 4p

h Wine gums 10p

i Sherbert 6p

j Refreshers 9p

4 Sequences

Finding missing entries in a number sequence (steps of 1, 2, 3, 5).

Write the missing numbers in each sequence.

Like this: 46 → 44 → w → 40 → x → 36 → w 42, x 38

17	18	a	20	21	b
43	c	41	40	d	38
8	11	e	f	20	23
20	22	g	26	28	h
15	i	25	j	35	40
k	45	l	41	39	37
37	34	31	m	25	n
70	65	o	55	p	45
q	13	r	7	4	s
92	t	96	98	u	102

5 4 coins

Investigating different possible coin totals when choosing from four coins.

You need **one** of **each** of these coins.   

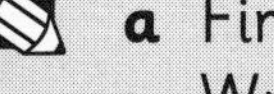

a Find amounts which can be made using these coins.
Write your answers each time.

Like this:

I can make 7p with 

I can make 13p with    

Answers

Page 2/3

1 Counting

a 7 b 5 c 6 d 1 e 3
f 8 g 8 h 2 i 9 j 6
k 7 l 3 m 9 n 4 o 10

2 Writing numerals

a 5 b 11 c 2 d 13 e 9
f 15 g 3 h 18 i 10 j 7
k 12 l 1 m 4 n 16 o 20
p 14

3 Stamps

a 3p b 5p c 7p d 2p e 8p
f 7p g 8p h 4p i 6p j 5p
k 9p l 6p

4 Put in order

a 1, 2, 3, 4, 5, 6 b 2, 3, 4, 5, 6, 7
c 3, 4, 5, 6, 7, 8 d 4, 5, 6, 7, 8, 9
e 5, 6, 7, 8, 9, 10 f 1, 3, 4, 5, 7, 8
g 2, 5, 6, 7, 9, 10 h 3, 4, 6, 7, 8, 9
i 1, 2, 5, 6, 9, 10 j 2, 3, 5, 6, 8, 10

5 Dominoes

a 1,1; 1,3; 1,5; 3,3; 3,5; 5,5
b 2,2; 2,4; 2,6; 4,4; 4,6; 6,6
c 1,2; 1,4; 1,6; 2,3; 2,5; 3,4; 3,6; 4,5; 5,6

Page 4/5

1 Number lines

a 2 b 5 c 11 d 16 e 18
f 3 g 6 h 12 i 17 j 19
k 23 l 27 m 33 n 36 o 39
p 21 q 25 r 29 s 32 t 37

2 Domino totals

a 5 b 10 c 7 d 5
e 6 f 8 g 10 h 7
i 8 j 3 k 9 l 6
m 4 n 12 o 6 p 7
q 8 r 9

3 Counting

a 2 b 7 c 8 d 1 e 6
f 7 g 5 h 3 i 4 j 9
k 8 l 5 m 9 n 10 o 6

4 Sequences

a 43 b 46 c 36 d 39 e 69
f 64 g 21 h 18 i 54 j 58
k 45 l 51 m 82 n 78 o 36
p 38 q 73 r 69 s 65 t 28
u 30 v 32

5 Stamps

9p: 2p, 2p, 2p, 3p; 2p, 2p, 3p, 2p; 2p, 3p, 2p, 2p; 3p, 2p, 2p, 2p; 3p, 3p, 3p
7p: 2p, 2p, 3p; 2p, 3p, 2p; 3p, 2p, 2p

Page 6/7

1 Adding

a 9 b 4 c 9 d 7 e 7
f 7 g 9 h 8 i 9 j 8
k 5 l 7 m 8 n 7 o 9
p 10

2 Adding coins

a 2p b 4p c 4p d 8p e 3p
f 10p g 3p h 6p i 7p j 5p
k 9p l 7p m 11p n 6p o 12p
p 15p

3 Counting

a 2 b 3 c 8 d 6 e 4
f 10 g 8 h 9 i 5 j 7
k 6 l 5 m 1 n 7 o 9

4 Put in order

a 10, 9, 8, 7, 6, 5 b 9, 8, 7, 6, 5, 4
c 6, 5, 4, 3, 2, 1 d 8, 7, 6, 5, 4, 3
e 7, 6, 5, 4, 3, 2 f 9, 8, 7, 6, 4, 3
g 10, 8, 6, 5, 3, 2 h 8, 7, 5, 4, 3, 1
i 10, 9, 7, 6, 5, 2 j 10, 9, 6, 5, 2, 1

5 Swapping

One strategy is to start with a swap which places the '1' in position, then the '2', and so on.

Page 8/9

1 Dice totals

a 9 b 8 c 6 d 6 e 9
f 5 g 7 h 10 i 8 j 7
k 5 l 12 m 9 n 6 o 7

2 'More' strips

a 7 3 4 9 5 10 2 8 4 6
b 14 18 16 12 19 20 15 11 17 13
c 8 14 5 18 12 7 16 4 15 10

3 Counting

a 7 b 2 c 8 d 6 e 3
f 4 g 11 h 1 i 5 j 8
k 9 l 6 m 9 n 5 o 7

4 Put in order

a 3, 7, 11, 13, 15, 17
b 7, 8, 9, 10, 11, 12
c 10, 11, 12, 13, 14, 15
d 14, 15, 16, 17, 18, 19
e 12, 13, 14, 16, 17, 18
f 5, 8, 11, 14, 15, 17
g 6, 9, 10, 13, 16, 19
h 8, 11, 13, 15, 17, 19
i 7, 8, 10, 12, 14, 16
j 13, 15, 16, 17, 19, 20

5 Domino totals

2 spots 1,1
3 spots 2,1
4 spots 3,1; 2,2
5 spots 4,1; 3,2
7 spots 6,1; 5,2; 4,3
8 spots 6,2; 5,3; 4,4
9 spots 6,3; 5,4
10 spots 6,4; 5,5
11 spots 6,5
12 spots 6,6

Page 10/11

1 Counting

a 3 b 6 c 8 d 2 e 7
f 8 g 5 h 1 i 10 j 4
k 7 l 5 m 9 n 6 o 10

2 Writing number names

a seven b fifteen c two
d twenty e twelve f six
g seventeen h three
i nineteen j ten
k 5 l 13 m 8 n 14 o 1
p 16 q 9 r 11 s 4 t 18

3 Adding

a 3 b 6 c 10 d 8 e 4
f 8 g 6 h 3 i 5 j 6
k 6 l 7 m 10 n 7 o 7
p 8 q 9 r 10 s 9 t 8 u 8

4 Jumping addition

a 6 b 8 c 8 d 10 e 9
f 7 g 8 h 7 i 8 j 10
k 8 l 10 m 9 n 9 o 7
p 5 q 9 r 10 s 5 t 9

5 Writing numbers

3 letters: 1, 2, 6, 10
4 letters: 4, 5, 9
5 letters: 3, 7, 8
6 letters: 11, 12, 20
7 letters: 15, 16
8 letters: 13, 14, 18, 19
9 letters: 17

Page 12/13

1 Counting

a 5 b 9 c 9 d 2 e 7
f 7 g 6 h 1 i 4 j 10
k 7 l 3 m 8 n 5 o 7

2 'Less' strips

a 7 1 4 9 2 6 0 3 8 5
b 16 11 9 18 14 19 12 15 17 13
c 6 14 9 16 18 11 8 12 19 7

3 Put in order

a 14, 15, 16, 17, 18, 19
b 12, 13, 14, 16, 17, 18
c 7, 8, 9, 10, 11, 12
d 3, 7, 11, 13, 15, 17
e 10, 11, 12, 13, 14, 15
f 6, 9, 10, 13, 16, 19

4 Ordering

a 23, 24, 26, 27, 28, 29
b 31, 33, 35, 36, 37, 38
c 61, 63, 64, 65, 67, 69
d 80, 82, 84, 85, 86, 89
e 40, 41, 43, 44, 46, 48
f 15, 27, 36, 41, 52, 63
g 34, 42, 59, 60, 84, 91
h 18, 27, 39, 46, 51, 62
i 59, 58, 57, 55, 53, 51
j 98, 96, 95, 94, 93, 92
k 79, 78, 76, 73, 72, 71
l 19, 18, 17, 16, 13, 11
m 63, 54, 46, 35, 24, 19
n 99, 82, 72, 65, 54, 43
o 50, 42, 39, 38, 36, 31
p 72, 63, 57, 52, 45, 43

5 Coins

6p: 2 coins: 5p, 1p
3 coins: 2p, 2p, 2p
4 coins: 2p, 2p, 1p, 1p
5 coins: 2p, 1p, 1p, 1p, 1p
6 coins: 1p, 1p, 1p, 1p, 1p, 1p

Page 14/15

1 Numbers to 10

a 2 and 8 b 5 and 5 c 4 and 6
d 6 and 4 e 3 and 7 f 4 and 6
g 8 and 2 h 1 and 9 i 4 and 6
j 5 and 5 k 9 and 1 l 8 and 2
m 7 and 3 n 3 and 7 o 6 and 4

2 Writing number names

a twenty-three b forty-two
c fifty-six d eighty-one
e thirty-four f sixty-seven
g fifty h seventy-three
i forty-five j ninety-four
k 18 l 75 m 35 n 84 o 43
p 97 q 58 r 26 s 26 t 31

3 Jumping subtraction

a 3 b 2 c 2 d 7 e 4
f 2 g 2 h 1 i 3 j 1
k 1 l 4

4 Card totals

a 8 b 6 c 7 d 10 e 9
f 9 g 6 h 7 i 9 j 7
k 8 l 9 m 8 n 8 o 9
p 10 q 9 r 10 s 10 t 10

5 Making 4

Ways of making 5:
1 + 1 + 1 + 1 + 1
1 + 1 + 1 + 2
1 + 1 + 3
1 + 4
1 + 2 + 2

Page 16/17

1 Place value

a twenty b two c fifty
d five e seventy f ten
g one h six i eighty
j seven k one l four
m thirty n seventy o eight
p ninety q seven r twenty
s nine t sixty u forty

2 Numbers 1 to 10

a 3 and 7 b 5 and 5 c 1 and 9
d 8 and 2 e 4 and 6 f 6 and 4
g 9 and 1 h 2 and 8 i 4 and 6
j 2 and 8 k 2 and 8 l 7 and 3
m 5 and 5 n 3 and 7 o 6 and 4

3 Sequences

a 10 b 16 c 29 d 35 e 44
f 35 g 18 h 26 i 84 j 72
k 39 l 24

4 Pictograph

a red b silver c 4 d 2 e 5
f 1 g 6 h 4 i 3 j 1
k 1 l 2 m 4 n 18 o 16

5 Adding

Total of 10
0 + 10, 1 + 9, 2 + 8, 3 + 7, 4 + 6, 5 + 5, 6 + 4, 7 + 3, 8 + 2, 9 + 1, 10 + 0

Total of 12
0 + 12, 1 + 11, 2 + 10, 3 + 9, 4 + 8, 5 + 7, 6 + 6, 7 + 5, 8 + 4, 9 + 3, 10 + 2, 11 + 1, 12 + 0

Page 18/19

1 Numbers to 20

a 7 and 13 b 12 and 8
c 6 and 14 d 13 and 7
e 8 and 12 f 14 and 6
g 9 and 11 h 15 and 5
i 5 and 15 j 16 and 4
k 3 and 17 l 10 and 10

2 Numbers lines

a 12 b 15 c 20 d 23 e 28
f 14 g 18 h 21 i 25 j 27
k 31 l 34 m 39 n 44 o 48
p 33 q 37 r 42 s 45 t 49

3 'More' strips

a 8 6 11 4 10 7 3 9 5 2
b 8 5 12 9 3 11 7 13 6 10

4 Prices

a 2p, 1p b 5p, 1p
c 5p, 2p d 1p, 1p
e 5p, 5p f 2p, 2p, 1p
g 1p, 1p, 1p h 5p, 2p, 2p
i 2p, 1p, 1p j 5p, 2p, 1p
k 5p, 1p, 1p l 5p, 5p, 5p
m 2p, 2p, 2p n 5p, 5p, 1p
o 5p, 5p, 2p

5 Dice sums

Total of 2: 1,1
Total of 3: 1,2
Total of 4: 1,3; 2,2
Total of 5: 1,4; 2,3
Total of 6: 1,5; 2,4; 3,3
Total of 7: 1,6; 2,5; 3,4
Total of 8: 2,6; 3,5; 4,4
Total of 9: 3,6; 4,5
Total of 10: 4,6; 5,5
Total of 11: 5,6
Total of 12: 6,6

Page 20/21

1 Writing numerals

a 48 b 29 c 74 d 53 e 12
f 87 g 35 h 93 i 40 j 66
k 55 l 31

2 Numbers to 20

a 6 and 14 b 13 and 7
c 4 and 16 d 10 and 10
e 2 and 18 f 12 and 8
g 17 and 3 h 1 and 19
i 11 and 9 j 7 and 13

3 Darts

a 9 b 8 c 8 d 6 e 8
f 10 g 9 h 6 i 7

4 Choosing numbers

a 2 + 4 b 4 + 1 c 5 + 2
d 3 + 2 e 4 + 2 f 3 + 4
g 6 + 1 h 3 + 5 i 6 + 3
j 6 + 2

5 Three piles

8 in three piles:
6,1;1; 5,2,1; 4,2,2; 4,3,1; 3,3,2
8 in two piles:
7,1; 6,2; 5,3; 4,4

Page 22/23

1 Clocks

a 2 o'clock b half past 4
c 7 o'clock d half past 1
e 3 o'clock f half past 10
g 6 o'clock h half past 5
i 11 o'clock j half past 3

2 'Less' strips

a 3 5 8 6 1 4 7 0 9 2
b 2 5 0 7 4 8 3 6 9 1
c 3 7 1 5 9 0 4 8 2 6

3 Place value

a seventy b four c sixty
d thirty e six f seventy
g seven h ninety i forty
j nine k two l sixty
m twenty n one o seven
p ninety q five r seventy
s six t sixty

4 Stamps

a 7p b 11p c 8p d 13p
e 9p f 10p g 12p h 8p
i 9p j 6p k 10p l 10p
m 14p n 12p o 11p p 7p

5 Card sums

16 different additions altogether:

1+2=3 2+3=5 3+4=7
1+3=4 2+4=6 3+5=8
1+4=5 2+5=7 3+6=9
1+5=6 2+6=8
1+6=7 2+7=9
1+7 = 8
1+8 = 9

Page 24/25

1 Ordering

a 30, 31, 33, 36, 38, 39
b 11, 12, 13, 16, 17, 18
c 52, 53, 55, 57, 58, 59
d 90, 93, 94, 95, 97, 98
e 70, 73, 75, 76, 78, 79
f 24, 35, 37, 41, 52, 63
g 18, 29, 38, 49, 51, 64
h 14, 25, 29, 37, 39, 45
i 83, 79, 72, 68, 64, 55
j 97, 95, 89, 81, 79, 74
k 28, 27, 26, 25, 24, 23
l 69, 68, 67, 66, 65, 63

2 Subtracting

a 2 **b** 6 **c** 4 **d** 7
e 6 **f** 8 **g** 2 **h** 9
i 5 **j** 4 **k** 2 **l** 7
m 2 **n** 5 **o** 1 **p** 3

3 Clocks

a 3 o'clock **b** half past 1
c half past 5 **d** half past 8
e 1 o'clock **f** half past 11
g 2 o'clock **h** 10 o'clock
i 4 o'clock **j** 6 o'clock
k half past 6 **l** half past 2
m 11 o'clock **n** 5 o'clock
o 9 o'clock

4 Writing numerals

a 45 **b** 27 **c** 96 **d** 53 **e** 13
f 78 **g** 36 **h** 64 **i** 82 **j** 7

5 Dice differences

difference of 0:
1,1; 2,2; 3,3; 4,4; 5,5; 6,6
difference of 1:
1,2; 2,3; 3,4; 4,5; 5,6
difference of 2:
1,3; 2,4; 3,5; 4,6
difference of 3:
1,4; 2,5; 3,6
difference of 4:
1,5; 2,6
difference of 5:
1,6

Page 26/27

1 Difference tables

a 1 1 2 **b** 1 1 5 **c** 2 1 5
4 2 1 3 1 7 3 2 6
5 3 2 5 7 1 1 2 2

2 Number split

a 40+9 **b** 80+4 **c** 20+8
d 70+3 **e** 10+7 **f** 50+1
g 30+6 **h** 60+0 **i** 90+5
j 40+2 **k** 50+3 **l** 10+5
m 30+1 **n** 20+7 **o** 70+0
p 40+8 **q** 80+2 **r** 60+6
s 90+4 **t** 50+9

3 Fewest coins

a 5p, 2p, 1p **b** 5p, 5p, 2p, 1p
c 2p, 1p **d** 5p, 5p, 5p
e 5p, 2p, 2p **f** 5p, 5p, 5p, 5p
g 2p, 2p **h** 5p, 5p, 2p, 2p
i 5p, 5p, 5p, 2p **j** 5p, 5p, lp
k 5p, 5p, 2p **l** 5p, 1p
m 5p, 5p, 5p, 2p, lp **n** 5p, 2p
o 5p, 5p 5p, 2p, 2p
p 5p, 5p, 5p, 5p, 5p
q 5p, 5p
r 5p, 5p, 5p, 1p
s 5p, 5p, 5p, 5p, 2p
t 5p, 5p, 5p, 5p, lp

4 'More' strips

a 13 16 20 15 19 12 18 21 17 14
b 15 18 20 13 21 19 14 22 17 16
c 18 20 16 19 17 23 21 14 22 15

5 Different additions

Six different totals are possible:
7, 8, 9, 10, 11 and 12.

Page 28/29

1 Subtracting

a 2 **b** 3 **c** 4 **d** 1 **e** 7
f 5 **g** 7 **h** 1 **i** 5 **j** 1
k 2 **l** 9 **m** 4 **n** 5 **o** 7

2 Clocks

a quarter past 2 **b** quarter to 2
c quarter past 4 **d** quarter past 6
e quarter to 4 **f** quarter past10
g quarter to 1 **h** quarter past 3
i quarter to 9 **j** quarter past 11

3 Sequences

a 15 **b** 30 **c** 40 **d** 25 **e** 60
f 85 **g** 30 **h** 60 **i** 70 **j** 60

4 Gaps

a six **b** two **c** twenty
d eighty **e** eight **f** three
g four **h** fifty **i** four
j sixty **k** three **l** thirty
m eighty **n** five **o** seventy
p seven **q** eighty **r** fifty
s two **t** six **u** forty

5 Domino differences

difference of 0:
1,1; 2,2; 3,3; 4,4; 5,5; 6,6
difference of 1:
1,2; 2,3; 3,4; 4,5; 5,6
difference of 2:
1,3; 2,4; 3,5; 4,6
difference of 3:
1,4; 2,5; 3,6
difference of 4:
1,5; 2,6
difference of 5:
1,6

Page 30/31

1 What's the number?

a 42 **b** 16 **c** 38 **d** 81 **e** 25
f 73 **g** 59 **h** 94 **i** 76 **j** 42
k 14 **l** 91 **m** 57 **n** 82 **o** 26
p 79 **q** 43 **r** 36 **s** 68 **t** 37

2 Strips of pairs

a 4 7 10 9 3 5 8 1 6 2
b 5 9 3 6 8 1 10 2 4 7
c 1 4 10 7 2 6 5 0 8 3

3 Adding

a 11 **b** 13 **c** 17 **d** 13
e 17 **f** 16 **g** 19 **h** 10
i 19 **j** 19 **k** 16 **l** 17
m 16 **n** 16 **o** 18 **p** 18

4 Jumping forwards and backwards

a 7 **b** 2 **c** 9 **d** 8 **e** 6
f 7 **g** 5 **h** 2 **i** 4 **j** 3
k 9 **l** 9 **m** 2 **n** 8 **o** 5
p 9 **q** 8 **r** 2 **s** 7 **t** 9

5 Writing numbers

5 letters: 40,50,60
6 letters: 11,12,20,30,80,90
7 letters: 15,16,70
8 letters: 13,14,18,19,41,46,51,52,56, 61, 62,66
9 letters: 17,21,22,26,31,32,36,44,45, 49,54,55,59,64,65,69,81,82,86
10 letters: 24,25,29,34,35,39,43,47,48 53,57,58,63,67,68,71,72,76,84,85,89
11 letters: 23,27,28,33,37,38,74,75, 79,83,87,88,93,97,98
12 letters: 73,77,78

Page 32/33

1 'Less' strips

a 11 15 13 18 10 16 19 17 12 14
b 11 14 17 12 18 15 10 9 13 16
c 8 13 15 11 9 14 16 10 17 12

2 Dice differences

a 2 **b** 4 **c** 2 **d** 0 **e** 1
f 4 **g** 0 **h** 2 **i** 2 **j** 0
k 1 **l** 1 **m** 1 **n** 1 **o** 0

3 Subtraction grids

a 3 8 1 **b** 1 7 3
0 4 7 5 4 0
6 2 5 8 2 6

4 Block graph

a blue b yellow c 3 d 5
e 4 f 6 g 2 h 3 i 3
j 1 k 2

5 Pairs

Total 16: 1+15, 2+14, 3+13, 4+12, 5+11, 6+10, 7+9

Total 15: 1+14, 2+13, 3+12, 4+11, 5+10, 6+9, 7+8

Page 34/35

1 Card differences

a 5 b 3 c 8 d 5 e 4
f 7 g 4 h 4 i 5 j 2
k 6 l 7 m 5 n 3 o 4

2 Number split

a 30+2 b 10+7 c 80+9
d 50+3 e 20+5 f 70+6
g 40+8 h 30+7 i 60+2
j 90+4 k 50+9 l 90+0
m 20+7 n 40+1 o 60+8
p 30+6 q 10+4 r 80+5
s 70+3 t 40+4

3 Clocks

a quarter past 3 b quarter to 10
c quarter past 6 d quarter to 7
e quarter past 1 f quarter to 4
g quarter to 9 h quarter past 2
i half past 2 j quarter to 2
k quarter past 10 l 8 o'clock
m quarter to 12 n quarter past 4
o quarter to 6 p quarter to 11
q quarter past 11 r quarter to 1
s half past 7 t quarter past 9

4 Gaps

a 4 b 2 c 5 d 2 e 9
f 7 g 5 h 5 i 7 j 6
k 3 l 4 m 2 n 7 o 1
p 3 q 6 r 7 s 5 t 5
u 5

5 Adding coins

Amounts possible with two coins are:
2p, 3p, 4p, 6p, 7p, 10p

Amounts possible with three coins are:
4p, 5p, 6p, 8p, 9p, 11p, 12p

Page 36/37

1 Darts

a 15 b 11 c 14 d 14 e 13
f 12 g 16 h 13 i 12

2 More or less

a 6 b 3 c 8 d 6 e 10
f 6 g 5 h 2 i 5 j 8
k 8 l 7 m 1 n 9 o 1
p 2

3 Card totals

a 14 b 19 c 17 d 15 e 17
f 19 g 14 h 18 i 18 j 16
k 20 l 15 m 16 n 20 o 16

4 Choosing numbers

a 9–3 b 7–1 c 8–3 d 9–5 e 6–2
f 5–3 g 8–2 h 4–2 i 6–4 j 7–3

5 Block graph

Drawing a block graph to show dice scores.

Page 38/39

1 Jumping addition

a 12 b 15 c 15 d 14 e 14
f 12 g 16 h14 i 14 j 18
k 18 l 15 m 12 n 17 o 18

2 Strips of pairs

c 6 12 1 15 4 17 8 11 18 7
b 15 7 19 2 9 16 3 11 5 13

3 Number lines

a 43 b 48 c 53 d 55
e 58 f 41 g 45 h 51
i 54 j 57 k 51 l 56
m 61 n 65 o 69 p 52
q 57 r 62 s 66 t 68

4 Swap two

a 24 and 22 b 57 and 55
c 74 and 71 d 21 and 16
e 25 and 23 f 40 and 36
g 90 and 88 h 52 and 47
i 38 and 37 j 45 and 36
k 56 and 35 l 71 and 63

5 Amounts of coins

Amounts possible with two coins are:
2p, 3p, 4p, 6p, 7p, 10p, 1 lp, 12p, 15p, 20p

Amounts possible with three coins are:
4p, 5p, 7p, 8p, 9p, 1 lp, 12p, 13p, 14p, 16p, 17p, 21p, 22p

Page 40/41

1 Adding

a 15 b 16 c 14 d 17 e 18
f 17 g 16 h 17 i 19 j 15
k 17 l 20 m17 n 16 o 19
p 13 q 16 r 19 s 19 t 18

2 What's the number?

a 44 b 67 c 31 d 89 e 13
f 76 g 25 h 94 i 52 j 68
k 34 l 19 m 73 n 95 o 21
p 86 q 67 r 52 s 38 t 43

3 Clocks

a 10 past 4 b 20 to 7
c 20 past 4 d half past 7
e 10 to 3 f 10 past 8
g 20 past 9 h 25 past 5
i quarter to 2 j 25 to 5
k 5 past 10 l 5 to 8
m quarter to 10 n 5 to 12
o 25 to 9

4 Adding machines

11 15 18 7 13 19 10 17 12 16
15 10 18 13 19 17 12 14 20 16
15 17 20 12 18 14 19 16 22 13

5 Making numbers

c In order: 34, 36, 43, 46, 63, 64

Page 42/43

1 Writing numerals

a thirty-seven b forty-five
c fifty-six d ninety-two
e thirty-four f fifteen
g sixty-five h twenty-one
i seventy-four j forty

2 Subtracting

a 11 b 5 c 13 d 14 e 10
f 3 g 13 h 7 i 12 j 13
k 8 l 11 m 15 n 9 o 9
p 14

3 Card differences

a 3 b 2 c 8 d 5 e 1
f 4 g 0 h 6 i 7 j 0

4 Adding coins

a 4p b 10p c 6p d 11p e 15p
f 2p g 7p h 12p i 3p j 20p
k 7p l 5p m 3p n 16p o 13p
p 4p q 8p r 21p s 12p t 11p

5 See-saws

1+2=3, 1+3=4, 1+4=5, 1+5=6, 1+6=7
2+3=5, 2+4=6, 2+5=7, 3+4=7

Page 44/45

1 How near?

a 25 b 87 c 28 d 25 e 52
f 72 g 58 h 82 i 25 j 25
k 82&78 l 52&28 m 28
n 87 o 28 p 52

2 Jumping subtractions

a 12 b 14 c 4 d 1 e 9
f 7 g 9 h 13 i 2 j 9
k 5 l 9 m 6 n 10 o 4
p 9

3 Taking away machines

a 14 6 10 7 17 2 4 15 3 8
b 3 7 5 12 1 4 10 6 2 8

4 Targets

a 16 b 15 c 20 d 13 e 18
f 14 g 18 h 12 i 16

5 Domino pairs

a: 2 spots and 8 spots:
1–1 & 4–4, 1–1 & 3–5, 1–1 & 2–6

3 spots and 7 spots:
1–2 & 1–6, 1–2 & 2–5, 1–2 & 3–4

4 spots and 6 spots:
1–3 & 1–5, 1–3 & 2–4, 1–3 & 3–4
2–2 & 1–5, 2–2 & 3–3, 2–2 & 2–4

1–4 & 2–3

c: 2 spots and 6 spots:
1–1 & 1–5, 1–1 & 2–4, 1–1 & 3–3

3 spots and 5 spots:
1–2 & 1–4, 2–2 & 2–3

4 spots and 4 spots:
1–3 & 2–2

Page 46/47

1 Change

a 8p **b** 5p **c** 6p **d** 9p **e** 7p
f 3p **g** 2p **h** 7p **i** 5p **j** 4p
k 4p **l** 6p **m** 1p **n** 4p **o** 2p
p 0p **q** 5p **r** 3p **s** 6p **t** 8p

2 Subtracting

a 13 **b** 17 **c** 11 **d** 13 **e** 17
f 8 **g** 7 **h** 17 **i** 5 **j** 10
k 12 **l** 15 **m** 14 **n** 6 **o** 15
p 3 **q** 5 **r** 3 **s** 7 **t** 6

3 More or less

a 6 **b** 8 **c** 7 **d** 19 **e** 7
f 17 **g** 9 **h** 11 **i** 9 **j** 15
k 14 **l** 5 **m** 17 **n** 8 **o** 15
p 9

4 Copying and completing a block graph from a set of data.

5 Arrows

2+2+2=6, 2+2+3=7, 2+2+5=9, 2+3+3=8, 2+3+5=10, 2+5+5=12, 3+3+3=9, 3+3+5=11, 3+5+5=13, 5+5+5=15

Page 48/49

1 Card differences

a 6 **b** 8 **c** 8 **d** 8 **e** 13
f 8 **g** 7 **h** 6 **i** 4 **j** 9

2 Swap two

a 35 and 37 **b** 95 and 94
c 57 and 54 **d** 46 and 44
e 91 and 83 **f** 32 and 29
g 52 and 49 **h** 95 and 83

3 Prices

a 1p, 2p **b** 10p, 2p
c 1p,1p **d** 5p, 2p
e 5p, 1p **f** 2p, 2p, 1p
g 1p, 1p, 1p **h** 5p, 5p, 1p
i 5p, 1p, 1p **j** 10p, 2p, 1p

4 Subtraction grids

a
9 5 2
3 10 8
7 6 4

b
12 8 2
6 1 10
3 11 4

c
3 16 5
4 8 1
7 12 1

d
13 18 8
10 2 15
16 11 17

5 Names

5 letters: James, Henry
6 letters: Thomas, Edward, Oliver
7 letters: William, Charles
8 letters: Nicholas
9 letters: Alexander
11 letters: Christopher

Page 50/51

1 How near?

a 14 **b** 95 **c** 14 **d** 19 **e** 49&51
f 59 **g** 59 **h** 94 **i** 15 **j** 14
k 91 **l** 41 **m** 19 and 41 **n** 91
o 41 **p** 45 **q** 54 **r** 59

2 Difference tables

a
3 8 15
10 1 8
16 5 2

b
13 4 1
10 1 2
7 2 5

c
7 2 13
3 8 3
1 4 7

3 'More' strips

a 40 70 20 90 50 100 30 110 80 60
b 55 63 41 21 82 106 14 73 96 33
c 44 61 75 22 109 85 37 113 92 53

4 Targets

a 4 **b** 7 **c** 8 **d** 6 **e** 2
f 8 **g** 6 **h** 9 **i** 6

5 Three dice

There are 10 ways:
1,1,1; 1,1,3; 1,1,5; 1,3,3; 1,3,5; 1,5,5; 3,3,3; 3,3,5; 3,5,5; 5,5,5

Page 52/53

1 Darts

a 13 **b** 13 **c** 19 **d** 17 **e** 18
f 14 **g** 17 **h** 16 **i** 15

2 Jumping forwards and backwards

a 9 **b** 10 **c** 15 **d** 13 **e** 12
f 17 **g** 15 **h** 6 **i** 8 **j** 12
k 19 **l** 11

3 Fractions

a $\frac{1}{2}$ **b** $\frac{1}{4}$ **c** $\frac{1}{2}$ **d** $\frac{1}{3}$ **e** $\frac{1}{4}$
f $\frac{1}{2}$ **g** $\frac{1}{2}$

4 Stamps

a 32p **b** 33p **c** 43p **d** 35p **e** 24p
f 36p **g** 30p **h** 27p **i** 38p **j** 40p
k 30p **l** 45p **m** 40p **n** 50p **o** 37p
p 32p

5 Difference pairs

difference of 9: 10,1; 11,2; 12,3; 13,4; 14,5; 15,6; 16,7
difference of 6: 7,1; 8,2; 9,3; 10,4; 11,5; 12,6; 13,7; 14,8; 15,8; 16,10

Page 54/55

1 Clocks

a 10 past 5 **b** 20 to 2
c 20 past 3 **d** 7 o'clock
e 10 to 7 **f** 5 past 8
g half past 2 **h** 25 past 11
i 25 to 3 **j** 10 to 2
k quarter past 9 **l** half past 6
m 20 to 9 **n** quarter to 4
o 5 past 4 **p** 5 to 6
q 25 past 10 **r** 20 past 4
s quarter past 7 **t** 10 past 12

2 'Less'strips

a 20 40 0 70 50 80 10 90 30 60
b 3 51 36 84 14 66 97 25 73 47
c 14 57 39 66 5 48 74 23 85 97

3 Addition tables

a
5 7 4
3 5 2
6 8 5

b
5 3 6
7 5 8
9 7 10

c
3 1 0
7 5 4
5 3 2

4 Card differences

a 7 **b** 5 **c** 8 **d** 3 **e** 1
f 2 **g** 8 **h** 5 **i** 6 **j** 10
k 1 **l** 4 **m** 5 **n** 2 **o** 7
p 7 **q** 5 **r** 3 **s** 8 **t** 3

5 Different subtractions

8–7=1, 7–6=1, 6–5=1, 5–4=1, 4–3=1
8–6=2, 7–5=2, 6–4=2, 5–3=2
8–5=3, 7–4=3, 6–3=3
8–4=4, 7–3=4
8–3=5

Page 56/57

1 Targets

a 8 **b** 10 **c** 6 **d** 9 **e** 10
f 10 **g** 4 **h** 11 **i** 7

2 Addition tables

a
[illegible] 17 19
[illegible] 14 16
[illegible] 11 13

b
12 10 15
19 17 22
13 11 16

c
12 16 13
16 20 17
11 17 14

3 Change

a 17p **b** 19p **c** 15p **d** 12p **e** 18p
f 13p **g** 16p **h** 10p **i** 14p **j** 11p

4 Sequences

a 19 **b** 22 **c** 42 **d** 39 **e** 14
f 17 **g** 24 **h** 30 **i** 20 **j** 30
k 47 **l** 43 **m** 28 **n** 22 **o** 60
p 50 **q** 16 **r** 10 **s** 1 **t** 94
u 100

5 Four Coins

1p: 1p
2p: 2p
3p: 2p, 1p
5p: 5p
6p: 5p, 1p
7p: 5p, 2p
8p: 5p, 2p, 1p
10p: 10p
11p: 10p, 1p
12p: 1op, 2p
13p: 10p, 2p, 1p
15p: 10p, 5p
17p: 10p, 5p, 2p
18p: 10p, 5p, 2p, 1p

Published by Collins Educational
An imprint of HarperCollins*Publishers*
77–85 Fulham Palace Road
Hammersmith
London
W6 8JB

First published 1995

Reprinted 1995, 1996, 1997

ISBN 0 00 312648–X

Author: Dave Kirkby

Illustrations: Juliet Breese, Jean de Lemos

Computer graphics: Alex Tucker, Peter Tucker

Design and typesetting: Alex Tucker, PGT Design, Oxford.

Printing: Scotprint, Musselburgh, Scotland.